NO UNCERTAIN
SOUND

For if the trumpet give an uncertain sound, who shall prepare himself to the battle?

I Cor. 14:8 (KJV)

NO UNCERTAIN SOUND

by

LILLIAN CUMMINS PROCTOR

Illustrated by

DELOR ERICKSON

AUGSBURG PUBLISHING HOUSE

MINNEAPOLIS, MINNESOTA

NO UNCERTAIN SOUND

Scripture quotations are from the Revised Standard Version of the
Bible, copyright 1946 and 1952 by the Division of Christian
Education of the National Council of Churches.

To my husband Fred Proctor
in appreciation for the many years
of happiness and love and laughter
we have shared.

Contents

Paul, the great defender of the Christian faith, having preached Jesus Christ, and him crucified and risen from the dead, in Palestine, in Asia Minor, in Europe, to both Jew and Gentile, returned to Jerusalem. He was arrested, scourged, and cast into prison as the Jews conspired to kill him.

The chief captain of the Jerusalem garrison, one Claudius Lysias, called two centurions and said to them, "At the third hour of the night get ready two hundred soldiers with seventy horsemen and two hundred spearmen to go as far as Caesarea. Also provide mounts for Paul to ride, and bring him safely to Felix the governor."

"And when Felix heard the accusations the Jews made, he deferred them and said, 'When Lysias, the tribune comes down, I will decide your case.'"

Letter From Lysias

Claudius Lysias, Tribune in the army of His Imperial Majesty, Tiberius Caesar, stationed in the land of Palestine . . .
To his father, the Most Excellent Marcus Lysias, teacher of philosophy in the city of Athens, Greece . . .
Greetings to you and my dearly loved mother:

Remembering the hot anger and resentment which were in all our hearts when I was assigned to this despised and turbulent outpost of the Roman Empire, and knowing that you will have received an official statement from the Roman Procurator, Pontius Pilate, informing you that because of my acceptable service here, I am to be permitted a choice as to my next assignment, knowing surely that you will have assumed that I have no other desire than to return to Athens, I am endeavoring to set down in orderly fashion things which will seem strange to you—perhaps incomprehensible.

I cannot tell when it began, or where—the strange urge within me for something beyond myself. I do not know when I first felt the need for a wisdom greater than that of my own father, and of a tenderness greater than my mother's arms. I am not sure of the moment when I found it—something strong, and sure, and steadfast, and beautiful.

As I endeavor to assemble and correlate the impressions and events of these years, memories fill me.

I find myself looking back upon events, upon people. Some of high social and political and religious prestige, some, not important in themselves, but like the heaps of stones one sees sometimes in the wilderness places of Palestine around which are twined the roots of a flawless flowering plant.

9

I remember Nicodemus and the affair of elegance at which we met, the supper party given by Pontius Pilate on my first night in Jerusalem. I remember Mariamne and my hand reaches out to touch her.

I remember Zoldi, the Egyptian tribune, with a yearning in him like my own, and Julius, tribune from the city of Rome. I think he had a yearning which was never satisfied.

I hold, as one holds carefully in his hands a box of precious ointment, the memory of hours spent in the home of Martha and Mary and their young brother Lazarus—poor indeed in material things but rich beyond accounting in the priceless possessions of love and loyalty and deep conviction.

I recall with nauseous clarity the birthday party in the city of Tiberias. Herod, the Tetrarch of Galilee. Herodias and Salome. I have only to close my eyes to see again the glitter and display, the lewd dancing and drunkenness, to hear again the raucous laughter and singing, and remembering how underneath were the surging, mounting emotions of hatred and vengeance culminating in monstrous murder, I shudder.

I do not forget Matthew and Susanna. Dear Susanna! I hear the thump, thump, thump of her heavy, clumsy foot, but recall that often she covered it with white leather and gay stones to hide it as she hid the sorrow in her heart because of it.

I remember sitting with eight men, cross-legged on the deck of a dirty boat anchored in the harbor of Gadara, eating freshly caught fish and hard rolls. I close my eyes, and find in my mouth the taste of nectar and ambrosia.

When I am grown old and all my other memories are gone, I shall not forget a dark, tragic, stormy Friday in Jerusalem. Susanna, for the first time dragging her heavy foot as if it had become an unbearable burden. Mariamne's eyes dark with tears. A little boy named Caleb breaking away from his mother's restraining hand and beating with his tiny fists on the legs of a Roman centurion, screaming, "You can not take my Jesus! You let him go, you soldier you!"

It was a feast day in all of Palestine, but those of us who sat in an upper room in the great house of Nicodemus at the hour of noon, knew only that the storm which had broken over the city and had turned the sky as black as midnight, was no more turbulent than the despair which filled our hearts.

These, my parents, are only a few of the things I wish to write. Perhaps if I begin with that April day, now three years gone, when I, an arrogant young Greek, rode into the city of Jerusalem, and write as I remember, the conclusion to my letter may be less difficult than I think.

That you will read with love, I know. I pray that you may read with understanding also . . . .

Jerusalem

A covey of chukar partridges ran along the side of the road in front of us, their red legs and bills like blood in the glaring sun—partridges like those my father and I hunted on the bend of the River Strymon outside Amphipolis every year when the season was right. Occasionally one would ruffle his richly barred feathers in the deep white dust as if he fancied himself splattering cool water in a pool.

Perhaps it was the pervading drowsiness of the early afternoon, the rhythmic, muffled flip-flop of the horses' hooves, the cooing of a wood-dove somewhere in the distance, the shrill insistent call of the cicadas. Perhaps it was the bluish-green leaves and yellow flowers of rue mingling lazily in the vagrant breeze to make a color on the fields like that on the river in the early dusk. Perhaps it was their warm, sweet perfume in the air. Warm and sweet like my mother's arms about me when we said farewell.

I looked at Tribune Zoldi, the Egyptian, riding beside me. I knew full well he saw no picture painted against the background of the almond trees awakening from their winter's sleep and flushed like a child with their pink and white blossoms. His mind was on the journey ahead, the common soldiers who rode a few paces behind us, and the fact that his own horse seemed to be limping a little.

But I saw it plain and clear. I saw my father, his beard like burnished bronze in the light of the campfire, his hunting dog with ears lifted even now that the chase was ended, lying contentedly with his head on my father's boot. I seemed to hear the gay laughter of my mother when my father, returning from a journey into Egypt, made for the purpose of examining cuneiform tablets

12

holding secrets of more than thirty dynasties before Alexander the Great, had brought a hunting dog named Rameses.

I wanted to speak to Zoldi about the hunting trips, about the dog purchased in his own country, but I would not. A new tribune in the army of Tiberius Caesar does not dare speak of nostalgic dreams.

The boat from Athens had docked early in the morning, and I was glad to be off the boat and on a horse again. The journey had not been a pleasant one. It was April, and the weather warm and humid. The boat, crowded and slow, had seemed filled with half the population of Italy and Macedonia as we made our way across the Mediterranean Sea, between Rhodes and Crete, past Cyprus, to the port of Joppa.

Five common soldiers, also replacements in the Roman army of occupation in Palestine, were aboard, and I feared they sensed the fact that I was not only young, but inexperienced, and less calloused than they. They indulged in numerous not very carefully hidden grins and nudges.

Tribune Zoldi and a small group of soldiers from the garrison in Jerusalem were waiting for us, the extra horses tethered nearby. I liked Zoldi immediately. A great bronzed man with black hair and startling blue eyes, so similar to my own that we laughed when we met.

The roads were crowded with travelers. Some walked and carried their needs for the journey in bundles strapped across their shoulders. Some had their bundles tied on the backs of stubborn, balky donkeys. Some pushed small two-wheeled carts. The men had brought goads for urging along the donkeys and the slow-moving cattle and sheep, but in the density of the crowd the long poles with their sharpened tips landed, more often than not, in the ribs of their fellow-travelers, and there was laughter and shouting and general good humor. Sometimes as we rode past, we heard them singing.

"Passover time," Zoldi told me, "one of the great annual feasts which lasts a full week, and which draws hundreds of thousands of visitors to Jerusalem. They come, not only from Palestine and Syria, but from the provinces of Galatia, and Cappadocia, and some from as far north as Bithynia and Pontus up near the Black

Sea. Many come by boat from my own land of Egypt, from your provinces of Achaia and Macedonia, and from the Roman capital itself."

"Jews?"

"Not the orthodox Hebrews of Palestine, but Jews nevertheless who seldom intermarry with foreigners and who have managed to maintain a stubborn sort of integrity as a nation wherever they live."

The sun was high when we reached Lydda, about eleven miles southeast of Joppa, and Zoldi stopped so that we might purchase food and fill our cruses with water. "We must eat in our hands," he said. "Jews are hospitable enough with their own people, but particularly in the small towns, Gentiles are considered far beneath them in any social relationships."

Riding along in the warm morning sunshine with my pleasant companion and with the common soldiers several paces behind, I had forgotten momentarily my aversion to this land to which I had come so unwillingly. Now my anger and resentment began to stir. Peasants! Considering themselves superior! Even the coarse bread made of beans mixed with some kind of grain seemed a personal affront. Zoldi glanced at me briefly. "Everybody hates it at first, Lysias," he said kindly.

The sun began to go down, and travel became less congested. Most of the pilgrims settled down for the night on the hard ground by the sides of the road. As long as it was light, we rode with care because of the children who scampered back and forth.

Zoldi halted our group and explained that he considered it wise for us to ride most of the night. Although one never doubted his authority, his manner was of such consideration that even the new recruits seemed to feel no resentment toward him. The night seemed long, but the soldiers sang as we rode.

The second day was not easy, and when we came to Emmaus, about seven miles out from Jerusalem, Zoldi ordered us to dismount, eat what was left of our food, and stretch ourselves on the ground for an hour's sleep. Remembering my own bed in Athens with its silken cushions and soft coverings, I was convinced that sleep would be impossible, but from the moment my cramped body touched the ground until Zoldi was shaking me awake, I could not have told whether I lay upon a bed in Athens or upon the hard soil of Palestine.

We entered Jerusalem by the Gate of Gennath, and in spite of myself, something of the excitement, the prevailing holiday spirit, stirred in my blood. Jews were everywhere—in the streets, in the doorways to the shops, examining the merchandise displayed in the flamboyant bazaars, pushing and thrusting each other aside as they tried to make their way to new places of interest.

Our horses plodded slowly through the crowds, past the business district, across the cobblestones of the praetorium square, to the northwest corner of the Temple area, to the Tower Antonia. This rather remarkable edifice of white marble with four imposing parapets had the general appearance of a castle, but I saw that it could be a formidable fortress as well. On the stairs, armed soldiers stood in full regalia, and in the cloisters, guards saluted stiffly.

Looking down from my window, I was suddenly aware of a new and different sound in the voices below. This was no holiday mood, but intense anger.

"Throw him out! Throw him out!" I heard them saying.

A man with a great scar across his cheek seemed to be their leader, urging them on. "You drive him out, Barabbas!" they shouted. "Take him before the Sanhedrin!"

"No!" Barabbas answered. "We can handle this ourselves!"

A knock at my door, and an aide speaking respectfully. "Tribune Claudius Lysias is requested to go to the Court of the Gentiles and quiet the disturbance there."

I did not understand the assignment. I did not like it. I stood still for a moment at the foot of the stairs, and looked at the excited throng of pushing, screaming Jews. If it had been possible, I would have joined any caravan going anywhere away from Palestine.

Four huge inside porches surrounded the paved area where the excitement was taking place, and as the crowd, led by Barabbas, seemed to be pushing toward the eastern porch, I joined them.

I looked in astonishment at the strange spectacle there. Crude stalls were built along the wall, and cages made of reeds. Low

tables with grooves cut into them were at one end. The gates to
the stalls were open as were the doors to the cages. The tables
were turned upside down, and spilling out over the floor, the silver
denarii bearing the superscription of Tiberius Caesar mixed in-
discriminately with the copper coins of Herod, Tetrarch of Galilee. Cattle and sheep pushed against me, and pigeons and doves
flapped their wings in my face.

The shouting seemed to be louder now and increasing in vol-
ume. The ones who shouted seemed determined to be rid of
someone.

I wondered what the malefactor had done. He must be hiding
now, I thought, behind one of the stalls or back of one of the up-
turned tables. A rough person, no doubt, since he must be respon-
sible for the debacle I viewed. I placed my hand on the hilt of
my sword.

He was not hiding. He walked calmly from the inner part of
the Temple, and the look on his face was not that of a marauder
or a man of violence. He was young, and yet there was an aura
of wisdom about him which made me think I must be mistaken
as to his identity.

The crowd was not mistaken. "Throw him out!" they advised
each other. "Drive him out of the Temple."

I decided as I watched that that was exactly what he was doing
to them—driving them out of the Temple, out of the Temple
court. He had a whip in his hands. But it was not much of a
whip. No man would have been afraid of it, even if he had stood
alone, and yet they were obeying his command.

"You are making of my Father's house a den of thieves," he
said repeatedly, and although he did not shout as they were
shouting, one heard him plainly.

I, a Roman soldier with a sword, understood their unwilling-
ness to oppose him actively. His strength was like no strength I
ever had seen. Not at all like the prowess of the brutish wrestlers
my friends and I had admired often in the Arena in Athens. It
was a quiet strength. It seemed activated and controlled by some
inner force.

His eyes drew mine and held them for a fleeting moment, and
in them I saw sternness, but I saw also the tender sadness which

one glimpses sometimes in the eyes of a father who punishes a
child, not willingly, but with love.

There was in this young stranger an element of poise, a kind
of dignity in spite of his peasant robes, which made me want to
know him. I had a sudden desire to sit down with him, to ask
him who he was, from whence he came, what purposes he held.
I felt sure he was a Jew, but strangely, it filled me with no displeasure.

There was a passing moment when I thought he was a Greek.

+   +   +

As I climbed the tower stairs, I thought the guards smiled, slyly,
as the recruits had smiled on the boat. One stopped me to say
that a messenger had come in my absence, bringing an invitation
from the Roman procurator, Pontius Pilate.

In Zoldi's quarters I found the tribunes enjoying their late
afternoon glasses of mesek, a pleasant drink which they told me
was wine mixed with spices. I saw the same sly smiles on their
faces which I had seen on the faces of the guards, and I decided
that my assignment had been an initiation to my new duties. Recalling similar occasions in my student days, I determined to
disappoint them by failing to mention my success or failure.

I wanted very much to ask about the young man in the Temple,
but instead asked the other question which now seemed of some
importance, but I was not prepared for the startling effect it
produced.

"I find that I have received an invitation to a supper party this
evening," I said. "The one to be given by Pontius Pilate, but I
cannot imagine a party which could compete with the pleasures
of a good night's sleep. Do you think it would be noticed if I fail
to attend?"

"Not attend!" they repeated almost simultaneously, and with
consternation. "You mean not go?"

"I mean not go," I answered. "I mean stay right here in my
own quarters and go to bed. Do you know how much sleep I got
last night? Surely one newly-arrived tribune would not be missed
in the midst of all the eminent visitors in Jerusalem."

Zoldi left his seat, came over to where I was standing, and put his hand on my arm.

"You go, Claudius Lysias," he said, "and in your finest array with your coral cape upon your shoulders. Never again let it cross your mind that you could dare refuse an invitation issued by the Roman procurator unless you are on your deathbed. When you grow more familiar with this business of soldiering mixed with politics, you will find that a little man in a place of authority, who is himself fearful of his superiors, is the most insistent about being obeyed. Keep in mind, my boy, that an insecure person is an inherently dangerous person."

"Surely you are not suggesting that the high and mighty procurator of this great land of Palestine is insecure!"

"He is indeed," one of the men stated positively. "It is whispered here in Jerusalem that except for his high-born wife, Pilate never would have received an appointment at all. He knows that these Jews hate all Romans, and that his slightest misstep would be reported to his immediate superior, Legate Vitellius of Syria, and when the report is relayed to Rome, Pilate's political career will be ended."

"I think you will enjoy the party, Lysias," Zoldi said, moving back to his chair. "Some of the spicier bits which we see in Pilate's parties in Caesarea are omitted here in Jerusalem because of the strait-laced Pharisees, but I wager you never will see anything equal to this in the way of entertainment."

One of the tribunes got up and began to refill the glasses, and I noticed the quick glance, and the slight movement of the eyelids exchanged by him and two of the others.

"One thing is certain," he said as he poured wine into the glass of a round-faced, boyish looking man whose name was Julius, "seeing the beauteous Salome dance will help you forget your fatigue. This damsel dances, my friend, she most certainly dances!"

When the other officers joined wholeheartedly in the laughter, I saw that the face of Julius held no laughter, but rather a dark, foreboding frown. I could see the knuckles pale and taut on his tightly clenched fists.

When I had returned to my room, I examined my uniform and my coral cape to see if they needed freshening for the party. I felt a rather pleasant sense of anticipation now. I felt I actually might like the tribunes, especially Zoldi, and I most certainly liked the idea of the new and exciting kind of entertainment. I looked forward to watching the beautiful girl and the kind of dancing I supposed they were conveying by their innuendoes.

Even though I had determined not to give the tribunes the satisfaction of hearing me mention the disturbance next door, I went back to Zoldi's quarters.

"You could not bear to leave us, Tribune Claudius Lysias, of Athens, Greece?" the man Julius asked with a not very carefully veiled sarcasm.

"Indeed I could bear to leave you," I answered, "but I saw a young man over in the temple . . . . "

"Jesus!" they all shouted.

"Then you know him?"

"Not really," Zoldi told me, "but lately it seems that everything we hear on the street corners, in the Temple, or even here in the tower has something to do with this young teacher. We have made a kind of game of it. Whenever someone mentions having been strangely impressed by a man new in Jerusalem circles, we shout his name, and so far we have not missed. He must have a dynamic personality to imprint himself so indelibly upon everyone with whom he comes in contact."

"Wait until those bigoted Pharisees begin to express their opinions," Julius said wryly.

"They will not like his popularity, that is certain," one of the others agreed.

"He was winning no popularity contest this afternoon," I told them. "All those men in the Temple were urging each other to throw him out. I could not understand any of it, why they were so bitterly against him or why all those animals and birds were in the Temple court."

"We took advantage of you, Lysias," Zoldi said. "We expected you to be confused. It takes a long time to understand this Jewish religion. This feast dates back two thousand years."

"About thirteen hundred years," Julius corrected him.

"Listen to him!" said one of the men. "Tribune Julius, the Roman, who hates the Jews because they will not bow down and worship his precious empire, and will not allow him to play the conquering hero, still knows all their beliefs and all their history!"

"And we know where he learns it," another added.

Again I saw the look of hatred pass over the boyish face, and the hard, tight fists.

"You do not know anything," he said. "I hate these Jews because to them the Romans are not conquerors! To them we are only puppets in the hands of their God! They consider themselves superior to us. To you too, Tribune Claudius Lysias. They know when we get a tribune who ought to have stayed longer with his mother, and who receives his position only because of his background! Sometimes, if you will turn suddenly, you will see them spit upon the ground!"

I was taken aback for a moment, but answered as pleasantly as I could. "Perhaps we should not look too quickly, Julius," I said.

"As for me," Julius continued, "I could kill them all!"

"All, Julius?" said one tribune laughing.

"If you want my opinion," Zoldi said, "I think the young man Jesus did a fine thing when he undertook to clean out the mess next door. Many years ago, Lysias, the Jews were in bondage in my own land of Egypt, and one of their great national heroes named Moses came to deliver them, but even after numerous plagues came upon my people, the rulers would not let them go.

"History says there came a dreadful night when, from the palace of the king to the house of the maid-servant down behind the mill, there was not a house in all Egypt in which there was not one dead. The first-born! The Jews obeyed their God and put the blood of a slain lamb on the lintels of their doors and the angel of death passed over them. It is that passing-over which they now celebrate."

"But what about the birds and the animals?"

"Every person who attends this feast must bring an offering. The wealthy bring the best of their flocks. The poor may bring only a pigeon or two young doves. A number of years ago some of the elders set up stalls and cages on the streets not far from the

Temple so those who came from a distance could purchase their sacrifices after they arrived in Jerusalem. As soon as it became apparent, however, that this was becoming a lucrative enterprise, the stalls and the cages were moved closer and closer to the Temple until finally they reached the place where you saw them today."

"They never miss a chance to put an extra coin in their pockets," Julius said, and I was relieved when he moved toward the door. The others followed immediately.

"Let me say this, Lysias," Zoldi said as he walked with me down the corridor, "you must not think that there are not many fine, earnest, sincere worshipers among the Jewish people. I listen often when I am standing guard in the temple to their scribes as they read from their history. I hear how their God transmuted even that bondage in my own country into a glorious sort of freedom. I hear how later they spent seventy years of exile in the land of Babylon, and as I listen I can see how their God used their ruined hopes and dreams, their loneliness and tears, to hew out a nation better fitted to his plans for them, how in exile he taught them things he never could have taught them in their days of prosperity.

"I tell you, Lysias, the bare austerity of their history intrigues me, and the deep indicatives which this God of theirs has laid down for them might well be worth any man's consideration and effort."

"It must be, Zoldi," I said, "that these Jews make their God seem more real than the gods and goddesses of your people or mine have ever seemed."

"I think it is because there is no doubt in their minds," he answered. "They do not always behave in accordance with their beliefs, but they never feel the need to prove their God. They will tell you that he sits upon the circle of the earth. They say he measured out the oceans in the hollow of his hand and weighed the mountains on a scale and the hills on a balance, that he pitched the blue sky like a tent for them to dwell in. Do you ever wish for a god like that, Lysias?"

"I feel no need of any gods at all," I answered.

✝   +   +

Before many hours had gone by, I was to learn that the glamorous and garish entertaining done by the Roman procurator had not been exaggerated. It was indeed a party to stir the imagination, and I thought that if the affairs which were given in Caesarea were more sophisticated or more lax than this, I could not greatly blame the strictly religious Pharisees for objecting.

I had attended many important functions given by the socially prominent and wealthy people of Athens, the less pretentious but highly correct affairs of the teachers, the gay and not too restrained dances of the student body, but never had I witnessed such obvious effort to impress, such vulgar display of decoration, jewels and apparel as I saw that night.

I had heard much of the man Pilate in my own home town of Athens as well as the rather uncomplimentary picture given by the tribunes earlier in the evening, and I was quite eager to see him for myself.

He looked like a man of about fifty, not very tall and with the paunchiness one associated with the rich diet of the Roman people. His hair was gray and cropped short. He was arrayed in a purple toga of a heavy lustrous material trimmed with wide, embossed gold bands. His gilded sandals were sprinkled liberally with precious stones.

The thing which impressed me most was the gigantic gold and amethyst ring on the forefinger of his right hand. It was as big as an oyster shell, and he seemed to wield it as one might wield a scepter. I thought of Zoldi's remark about a little man in a place of authority.

In the place of honor with Pilate and his wife Claudia stood Herod, Tetrarch of Galilee, and his wife Herodias. Although on the surface there seemed to be friendliness and congeniality between these two important couples, it was apparent to me, as I watched them with interest, that underneath something unpleasant was stirring.

Herod seemed to be slightly older than Pilate, and in direct contrast to Pilate's apparent feeling of insecurity, was suave and self-assured. He had a certain obsequious manner, however, which led one to feel a lack of confidence in him. It was as if his carefully arranged hair and beard, which glistened with perfumed unguents, gave to his whole personality a vague connotation of oiliness.

I had a feeling that it might have been in order to show forth Pilate's costly toga as a vulgar display, that Herod's robe, although obviously as expensive as Pilate's was of the finest pure white linen and was decorated only with one band of deep blue. He wore no jewelry, and it seemed to me he used his hands much more than was necessary so that no one could fail to notice the contrast.

It was quite late in the evening, and the tribunes and I were standing somewhat apart from the other guests, our glasses in our hands, when suddenly Zoldi put his arm about my shoulder, and his lips close to my ear.

"Look, Lysias!" he said. "The distinguished gentleman who is just making his arrival at Pilate's party, is about the only man in Palestine, Jew or Gentile, who would dare to come at this hour."

"Who is he?" I asked.

"His name is Nicodemus, and he is most highly regarded by the Romans as well as by the Jewish people. He is a member of the Jewish supreme court, which is called the Sanhedrin, but in addition to being an outstanding jurist, he is also one of the greatest educators of our time. He and Gamaliel, whom you see standing in the receiving line with Pilate and Herod and the others, are considered the most erudite gentlemen on this side of the Mediterranean. This Gamaliel, however, would not dare to arrive so late."

I glanced momentarily at Nicodemus, but that which interested me most was Pilate. The expression on his face was a mixture of anger and humiliation. It was as if he knew—and hated the knowing—that this important personage had not considered his invitation to be of sufficient moment to have arrived in time to stand in the place of honor beside the others.

I saw the glance of gloating elation which Herodias gave to Claudia. I saw the spurious pat of sympathy on Claudia's arm. Even across the room, I could see the red blood rise like a crimson tide from Claudia's plump neck to the edge of her bejeweled hair. Pilate's hand with the great gold and amethyst ring waved back and forth almost incessantly.

It was a matter of tremendous surprise to me and to the other tribunes when the important personage of whom they had spoken so highly and with such unfeigned admiration, as soon as he had concluded greeting those who were in the receiving line, made his way across the great room to where we were standing.

He came directly to me, placed his hand on my shoulder, and said, "I happened to hear your name mentioned as one of the new replacements, and since I have seen these other gentlemen on many other such occasions as this, I feel sure you must be Tribune Claudius Lysias of Athens."

"I am, sir."

"I have long been an admirer of your father, Tribune," Nicodemus continued, "and if these gentlemen will excuse us, I should like a bit of conversation with you if we can find an unoccupied spot. Shall we try this balcony outside the window?"

Before I could answer, there was a fanfare of trumpets, and amid a wild burst of applause, into the center of the room a girl danced on tiptoe. It was as if she floated, or was blown there, by a warm and caressing wind. Her long black hair against the pure white of her diaphanous costume, her grace, and her exquisite beauty, almost took my breath away.

It was not so with Nicodemus.

"Salome!" he whispered. "Beauteous daughter of Herodias! Always she dances! I had hoped to miss, not only Pilate's indigestible food, but his threadbare entertainment!"

Threadbare, I repeated to myself. Not from where I stand.

"Hurry!" he urged me. "If we move quickly, we may be able to get out before the applause is over."

As we settled ourselves on a bench outside the balcony, it occurred to me, as it had often before, that being the son of gentle people sometimes presents definite disadvantages.

Inside, there was laughter and applause and music which stirred the blood. Inside, a beautiful girl in a filmy costume was performing a dance which the tribunes had led me to believe would be far from pastoral. Yet here I sat with an engaging gentleman the age of my father and supposed there was nothing I could do about it.

"I have read many of your father's books, Tribune," Nicodemus was saying, "and I consider him the greatest living teacher of philosophy. Besides, I happen to know he is a most eloquent silent orator."

I glanced at Nicodemus quickly, not understanding what he meant or caring too much, but I saw there was a twinkle in his eyes.

"I know of course, that your father is in much the same position as I am," he said. "Having obtained our Roman citizenship at a price, we still are not considered by the Romans as qualified to speak in their courts. This may seem unfair, but actually it has created for men like us a dignified and lucrative side-profession in serving as logographers."

"I believe I am not familiar with the word, sir."

"A speech-writer, my boy, a speech-writer for the less gifted. The last time I visited in Rome, people all over the city were loud in their praises of the stirring oration delivered in the Senate by my close friend, Polyemarcus. He confessed to me when he was in his cups that the speech had been written for him by your father, and I was convinced that he must be a man of wit as well as of learning."

"He is indeed, sir," I answered.

"I thought so!" said Nicodemus. "Polyemarcus let me read the speech, and it was so like the man himself—magniloquent, pompous, bombastic—that I felt sure your father had written it with his tongue in his cheek. I could tell he realizes, as I do, that since the transference of the seats of the mighty to Rome, the conquered have been, and continue to be, the teachers of the conquerors."

I crossed and uncrossed my knees. I changed positions until I was afraid he would see me—or would not. I ran my hand back and forth across my chin, and tugged at my ear, but Nicodemus was happy and relaxed. In spite of the fact that I wished to be inside Pilate's banquet hall, I liked this man. At some other time, I told myself, I should have considered him most engaging and entertaining. It is not easy to compete with a beautiful girl who dances.

"One thing in your father's books which I have not been able to understand," he went on, "is that he denies the existence of a Creator, but still finds it reasonable to believe in a multitude of gods, who though blissfully happy themselves, take no interest in the affairs of us poor, weak, struggling mortals."

I wondered if something in the way of a polite argument might lessen his desire to continue.

"You do not so believe, sir?" I asked.

"I do not indeed!" Nicodemus answered. "I believe in a God who is primarily a Creator. I believe that he created man, as well as the earth, the sky, the sea, and every living creature. I believe that while my God is of such majesty and power he could reach forth his hand and snuff out this whole world, as Pilate's servants will snuff out his candles ere this night is gone, he is of such gentleness and infinite understanding that the poorest slave, waiting to be sold in the public market, is of as great concern as the most regal king."

"You make your God sound most enticing, sir."

"Not enticing!" Nicodemus was quick to correct me. "He is no careless deity, too indulgent or eager for praise, to bring judgment upon those he rules. He is a father, close and infinitely loving, but also infinitely wise. While his judgments of his children are always encircled by his love, they are nevertheless sure and without deviation."

Without reason, I remembered the young man in the Temple. I remembered the stern displeasure in his voice, and the whip in his hands. I remembered the look of tender sadness in his eyes. Something like Nicodemus' God, I thought.

"Do you know a man named Jesus?" I asked him.

"Many men are named Jesus," he answered, evidently thinking that I was changing the subject.

"My boy," he said rising, "I apologize! Here it is your first view of the extravagant entertaining done by the Roman procurator, and I keep you on a balcony away from all the excitement, listening to a Jew talk about his God. In a little while Salome will begin another dance, and while she sends no red blood coursing through my veins, you are young. It is possible that you may have another viewpoint."

"I have enjoyed the conversation, sir," I told him and felt a small surprise when I realized that I meant it.

"You are a success!" Zoldi whispered in my ear when I had

woven my way through the crowd to where the tribunes were standing. "I have been in Jerusalem sixteen years, and Nicodemus has never accorded me—or any of the Roman officers—more than a casual greeting."

"The fatal charm of Tribune Claudius Lysias of Athens, Greece!" said Julius. "The great Nicodemus would not lift me from a ditch if he saw me lying in it."

I felt a need to defend Nicodemus as if we had been close friends for years.

"I think he would, Julius," I said.

The fanfare of trumpets sounded again, and Salome entered the hall. This time she did not seem to float. The drinks served at the beginning of the evening had been the pleasant juice made from pomegranates, but I had seen the huge golden bowls of arrack, the potent, fermented juice from the spathe of the date palm.

I could see that Salome's glasses had not been filled with mesek or pomegranate juice. She was dancing now with complete abandon.

As we joined in the deafening applause, one of the tribunes shouted, "It's just as well you waited, Lysias. This Salome gets better as the evening goes by!"

Julius began to push his way through the crowd, and I saw him going outside onto the balcony where I had sat with Nicodemus. He had a strange look in his eyes, and I shouted to Zoldi, "Is Julius sick?"

"Yes," Zoldi answered, "he is sick, but leave him alone."

The life of a soldier, particularly that of a superior officer in the Roman Army of Occupation, is for the most part an easy life. If one can obtain an assignment to a pleasant climate, among people having the same background, and the same ideas and ideals of educational and cultural values as one's own, the designated period in a country may terminate in something resembling a vacation more than a vocation.

These things were in the aspirations of my father when he used a bit of influence in high places to obtain such an assignment for me. But not here. "Assignment: Palestine," my parents and I had read, with horror. And yet I could not deny to myself the caustic enumeration Julius had made of my lack of age, experience, and soldierly toughness.

As I lay on my couch the morning after Pilate's supper party, however, I thought of how different the assignment promised to become. I was finding I liked the five other tribunes, even Julius. I thought with pleasure of my enforced conversation with Nicodemus and considered him a man comparable to my own father and my father's colleagues in Athens.

I stretched my arms high above my head, and thought of the exotic dancing of the beautiful Salome. It seemed entirely possible that I was going to like Jerusalem.

There was a knock on the door, and Tribune Julius entered with breakfast for two on a huge tray. If Pilate himself had entered bearing gifts, I could not have been more surprised.

"Good morning," he said, with nothing in his voice to give a clue as to whether he had come as friend or foe.

"Good morning," I answered.

His first remark was surprising and entirely foreign to anything he had said to me. "I am glad you have come to Jerusalem, Tribune Lysias," he stated positively. "My associates here at the tower do not understand me at all."

"You think I do?"

"You could," he said. "Prop yourself up with your pillows while I draw up a stool and we will eat our breakfast. I am an early riser," he added, managing to insert an accusing note into the remark, "and I have been waiting for a long time."

I remembered something I once had heard my father say to my mother. "How is it," he asked, "that some people have the devastating ability of always making one feel guilty?"

Julius applied himself immediately to the breakfast, and ate so silently, sitting with a look of preoccupation on his face when he had finished, that I felt the need to make some effort at conversation.

"Did you enjoy the party last night?" I asked as an opening wedge.

"No," he replied, flipping the seed of a grape across the room with a sort of personal vindictiveness.

The wrong approach, I decided. "I was interested in the guests," I told him. "This Herod, Tetrarch of Galilee, is he the one I have heard referred to as the king of the Jews?"

"He is not," said Julius, getting up and taking the tray of empty dishes to the door and shouting for an aide.

I thought I had lost again, but he came back in, tilted his stool at a precarious angle against the wall, and launched into this subject with apparent interest.

"This present Herod," he said, "is the son of that Herod who was called king of the Jews and who is also designated as Herod the Great. The entire family are demons!"

"Jews!" I agreed.

"No," Julius corrected me. "Not orthodox Jews. They are Idumeans, descendants of Esau rather than Esau's twin brother Jacob."

"That is bad?"

"To the orthodox Hebrews it is! The people here hated that Herod every day of the almost fifty years he reigned, from the time he was sent here by Julius Caesar as a procurator in Galilee to the day he died about thirty years ago."

"He was not actually a king at all then?"

"Oh yes, for whatever it means. When Julius Caesar was murdered, the Jews used the confusion in Rome for extensive rioting, and Herod—only fifteen years old—went fleeing to the Roman capital. About two years later he was returned to Palestine and was given the title of king."

Julius seemed pleased with his role as instructor, and I decided not to interrupt. Tossing back my covers, I got up off my couch and began to get dressed for the day. He did not seem to notice. He lowered his stool, walked to a nearby table, poured himself a glass of water, and after he had drunk it, took up his explanation where he had left off.

"The Jews hated that Herod because they considered him a usurper, because hoping to cement his relations with them, he married the great-granddaughter of one of their national heroes, and then, tiring of her and suspecting her of intrigue, had her murdered. They hated him for himself. Constantly apprehensive of losing his high position, he was cruel, conniving, and suspicious.

"Did you ever hear, Lysias, that about thirty years ago, shortly before he died, this Herod the Great heard that a new king of the Jews had been born in the little town of Bethlehem about five miles from Jerusalem, and was so terrified he had every baby boy there and in the surrounding country put to death?"

"I am shocked, Julius!" I told him, sitting down on the edge of my couch. "This man Herod whom I met last night seemed far removed from that sort of behavior. Is he as hated as his father was?"

"I hate him!" said Julius, letting the legs of his stool hit the floor with a resounding thump.

His lips were held tight for a moment and his face clouded with something I could not understand.

"Perhaps the people do not feel toward him as they felt toward Herod the Great, but they look with great disfavor upon him and upon the ambitious, scheming Herodias. Both this Herod and his brother Philip were educated in Rome and spent more time there than in their own land. Philip built himself a town-house and married a popular widow in the capital city. Herod was at that time married to the daughter of the Arab king Aretas, but once when he and his wife were visiting Philip, Herod developed a guilty passion for Herodias, divorced the Arab girl, and married his brother's wife.

"There has always been enmity between the Jews and the Arabs and war ensued in which the Jews suffered great losses. The people have never forgiven Herod—or Herodias—and look with stern disapproval upon the relationship between them."

"Is divorce not recognized in Palestine?"

"Oh yes! It is not the divorce to which they object. The Jews have a law which demands that if a man dies, his brother must take his widow as a wife, but for a man to be married to his brother's wife while that brother is living, is to them the same as if he lived with her in open adultery."

Julius rose suddenly, and walked to the door. I thought for a moment that he was going to depart as unceremoniously as he had arrived, but he paused, and turned back to me.

Again I was impressed with the childlike countenance, his round face and rosy cheeks making him look much younger than he was. I felt older than he, and had the strange impulse to encourage him as he seemed to want to say something but lacked the courage.

"Tomorrow is Saturday, the Jewish sabbath," he said, leaning over and carefully picking up the grape seed from the floor, "if you have no other plans, perhaps we could walk about Jerusalem and I could show you some of the places of interest."

Recalling the pushing, crowding throngs of visitors on the streets of Jerusalem, I thought that tomorrow the Tower of Antonia would probably seem like a haven of rest, but the childlike face, the hesitant manner, seemed to have me in their grasp.

"That would be pleasant, Julius," I told him.

"What about your soldierly toughness?" I muttered under my breath as he walked down the hall.

Evening Meal With Nicodemus

When Passover week was over, when the excitement had died down, and the crowds of visitors had returned to their homes, Jerusalem did not seem greatly different from other cities. The living quarters of the soldiers in the Tower Antonia were extremely pleasant, and the quarters for the tribunes almost luxurious. The huge gymnasium was within easy walking distance, and we tribunes spent most of our evenings there, watching or taking part in the foot racing, boxing, wrestling, quoit pitching, or javelin-throwing.

The strictly religious citizens looked upon this place of amusement with abhorrence, not only because it had been erected during the time when Palestine was under the dominion of Syria and when Antiochus Epiphanes had tried to destroy the Jewish religion, but many parents contended that the games which took place there were corrupting the youth of Jerusalem. The fathers went to the priests complaining that their young men were wearing the winged cap of the Greek god Hermes when they ran in the foot races, and that they exercised naked on the stadium courses. It was rather widely known by those who attended the games that the priests showed no great zeal in the matter for the very simple and understandable reason that they spent much time there themselves.

Within a week after our conversation on the balcony outside Pilate's banquet hall, Nicodemus had begun to invite me to be a guest in his home. His wife and daughter were visiting in Rome, but his well-trained staff of servants prepared and served delicious meals to the two of us. In spite of the difference in our ages, we were most compatible, and I found myself being drawn to him more and more. My admiration for him was not only for his intellectual achievements which appealed to me so strongly, but for a kind of innate integrity, a continuing rightness of attitude toward people and concerning events.

I could not decide whether to feel complimented or annoyed because of the fact that Tribune Julius seemed to be almost constantly by my side. He found strange excuses for visiting my room or for walking where I happened to be walking. As we sat watching the games in the gymnasium, he managed somehow always to be sitting beside me. Zoldi, with his kindly interest in the entire garrison, from the tribunes to the most pugnacious of the common soldiers, urged me to accept whatever advances Julius made toward friendliness, to ignore his caustic remarks, and to endeavor to give him help.

"Julius needs a friend, Lysias," he said to me. "I never have known a man who needs a friend so much. He would not like the comparison, but he reminds me of the palmer worm which wanders from place to place like a pilgrim, and never finds a place of abode."

"I should hate to think he would take up his abode with me," I said.

Zoldi laughed. "He will not, Lysias. I think Julius will never learn how to allow himself to come close to anyone."

One evening in the last part of May, as we sat in the stadium watching a group of uncommonly fine foot racers from Damascus, Julius said to me, "Have you heard of the strange preacher called John the Baptist?"

"No," I answered shortly, not wishing to miss any part of the contest.

"We are free tomorrow. I will prepare the lunch, and we will go out to the wilderness by the Jordan River where he preaches."

"Yes," I answered, wishing only to have the conversation terminated.

Early the next morning, Julius knocked on my door. "Are you ready?" he called.

"Ready for what?"

"To go out to the wilderness to hear the preacher. I have the lunch. We must start immediately."

Except for the fact that I remembered Zoldi's words about Julius' needing a friend and his comparison of Julius to the wandering palmer worm, I should have pulled the covers over my ears and dismissed the matter from my mind. Instead, I got up sleepily and began to dress. "I have had no breakfast," I told him in my most surly manner.

"I have it here on a tray," he answered. "Open the door."

We went to the wilderness, and I was amazed at the multitude who thronged both the banks of the Jordan River and the wild, uninhabited country on either side. In a shallow inlet I could see a man of thirty or thirty-five years, with numbers of people around him. He was taking them one by one, placing his strong arms under their shoulders, and letting them down into the water. They came up choking and coughing but seemingly happy, and those who stood on the edge of the banks were calling out, "Me next, Prophet! Me next!"

"What is all this?" I asked Julius as he urged me forward until we stood within a few feet of the water. I regretted having let him persuade me to mix with such a crowd so early in the morning.

The angry, trampled nettles stung my ankles, and the insistent gnats swarmed about my nostrils and the corners of my mouth. A thin, dirty man standing next to me leaned over, looked intently at his dirty leg, wet his forefinger with his tongue, lifted a flea from his ankle and cracked it between his thumb nails.

Just as I was about to say to Julius that he might stay if he wished but that I was going back to the city, there was a definite stir in the crowd, and all eyes were turned away from the ceremony taking place in the water to a man who rode into the very midst of the throng and halted his great black steed on the river bank. I could scarcely believe my eyes. It was Herod. He was a striking figure in his black tunic, black riding breeches, and red boots. He tapped with his silver studded riding whip those who stood too near, and although there were angry mutterings, the crowd moved away, so that he sat on his horse in a little island of clean sand and rocks.

Julius put his mouth close to my ear. He spoke so low I could barely hear his words. "He comes here every day," he said.

"Have you been here before, Julius?" I asked.

"I also come every day."

Even with Herod's presence giving tone to the scene, I was determined to leave, but the preacher called John the Baptist held up his hand for quiet, and he began to talk. He had wrapped about him a loose, coarse cloth held in place by a leathern strap. He was a lean, wiry man, and almost unbelievably intense. His voice was deep and resonant.

There was a kind of thunderous beauty in his words. I saw his piercing black eyes turn toward Herod, and I saw Herod move about a bit and change the reins of his expensive harness from one hand to the other.

"Prepare the way of the Lord!" John said. "Make his paths straight! Every valley shall be filled, and every mountain and hill shall be brought low, and the crooked shall be made straight, and the rough ways shall be made smooth; and all flesh shall see the salvation of the Lord!"

A heckler with a smirk on his face called out, "Who are you? Are you the Christ?" John answered him plainly, "I am not the Christ."

"Well then," the man persisted, "are you Elijah, who will come before the Christ comes?" John replied, "I am not."

"Are you then that prophet of whom Moses spoke?" he asked, and John answered curtly, "No."

It was while this was taking place that a group of obviously important men rode in on their horses and stopped directly behind Herod. The numerous phylacteries bound about their arms and their foreheads made me think they were members of the party of the Pharisees whom I had come to recognize in Jerusalem. John saw them, and his beautiful and lofty words seemed forgotten. He spoke directly to them.

"You vipers!" he said. "You brood of vipers! Who warned you to flee from the wrath to come? You say to yourselves, 'We have Abraham as our father, and we need nothing more.' I tell you, God could raise up children to Abraham out of these stones!"

The Pharisees did not like this. They talked behind their hands. One could see that the people were troubled that John should single out these influential men, but one could also see that they were moved by his words. One man standing on the other side of the river picked up a stone, looked at it intently, and pitched it into the water near the place where Herod and the Pharisees sat on their horses. "What shall we do then?" he shouted.

The whole crowd of the poor, the unwashed, the nobodies, took it up. "What shall we do?" they cried. "If being the children of Abraham is not enough, what shall we do?"

John had the answer. "Behave as the children of Abraham ought to behave! If you have two coats, give one to the man who has none. If you have meat to eat, share with those who have nothing."

A group of wealthy-looking Jews had taken their place near Julius and me. "Looks like only the poor come early," I said. "Who are these newcomers?"

"Tax-collectors," Julius answered.

After listening to John for a while, they began to call out, "What ought we to do?"

"Do not collect more taxes than the Roman government requires and then put it in your own pockets."

Loud in my ears, I heard the voice of Tribune Julius of Rome. "What shall we do?"

I put my hand on his arm. I did not like having him call attention to us. John searched the crowd with his eyes until he saw us, and he answered as plainly and as fearlessly as he had answered his own people. "You Gentiles, you Roman soldiers," he said, "do no violence to any man. Accuse no man falsely. Be content with your wages."

There was a lull in the voices now. People were looking at Julius and at me with suspicion in their faces. They thought there was trickery afoot, that we had come to spy on them. Some of them moved away from where we stood. Suddenly, however, they lost all interest in us. The important Pharisees were speaking. They asked no questions about what they should do. Zoldi had told me that he had heard them often publicly thanking God that they were not like other men, and I could see the smugness, the self-satisfaction in their faces.

"Why are you baptizing if you are neither the Christ nor Elijah nor the prophet?" they demanded.

It was evident that the authoritative questioning of this important deputation troubled John the Baptist no more than the questions of the poor or the tax-collectors or the sudden question of Tribune Julius.

Even now, I cannot remember how the next events happened. I am sure I did not actually see the child as he fell into the deep part of the river. I know I made no decision to save him. I only remember being in the water, bringing him out—wet and limp and gasping for breath.

I was far from being prepared for the reaction of the crowd. Mothers began to cry and kiss my hands. The evil-smelling men, redolent of their leeks and garlic, put their arms around my shoulders. Herod caught my eye and made a slight gesture of approval, and the Pharisees nodded their heads in commendation.

I stood there—wet and uncomfortable and embarrassed.

Across the heads of the milling, excited throng, moving quietly among the people, I saw the tall young man I had seen in the Temple. I thought he smiled.

At the Tower a servant had brought an invitation to the home of Nicodemus for the supper hour. As I finished dressing for my engagement, an aide announced that a woman had come looking for me. She lingered on the court, he said, and would not leave.

She was poorly dressed, and her face was sweet and gentle and stained with tears. "I am Hannah, sir," she said. "It was my small son Caleb you saved from the river. I bring you soup, sir, made from lentils. It will make you warm after your ride in the wet clothes. May the Lord bless you, sir, and keep you. May he make his face to shine upon you!"

Remembering well the acrimonious tongue of Julius, but not willing to have this gentle woman know- I would not eat the soup, I thanked her, and climbed the stair with the earthen pot in my hands.

+ 	+ 	+

When I reached the gate to Nicodemus' estate and looked down the long graveled roadway to the great bronze doors flanked on either side by huge white marble urns, I felt again the warm sense of anticipation which I had always felt when I was to spend an evening with him. I thought how strange it was that in all the time I had spent with Nicodemus in the two months I had been in Jerusalem, I had given so little thought to his family. I knew that he had a wife and a daughter who were visiting in Rome, but that seemed to have been an end of it.

Perhaps it was because I enjoyed Nicodemus so greatly for himself. We could spend long evenings together, much as my father and I always had done, and never seem to grow tired of our subjects or of hearing each other's opinions. I often had heard it said that the Greeks emit philosophy as naturally as they breathe, and I had decided that so also did the Jews.

On this evening Nicodemus opened the doors, his wife and his daughter Mariamne standing beside him. I could see the happiness in his face, and in theirs. Immediately, I wished my own mother could see them. She never would have believed it, I thought.

They began almost at once to speak of the incident at the riverside. "It was a fine thing you did, my boy," Nicodemus said. "After the spring torrents, the waters in that part of the Jordan are dangerous indeed."

His wife touched my arm gently. "We are a volatile people, Tribune Lysias," she added, "sometimes unreasonably excitable, but I think the appreciation which is felt all over the city tonight by the rich and poor alike is something which will not be quickly forgotten."

I saw Mariamne's smile of understanding when I began to speak of the unusual and interesting preacher John the Baptist. Nicodemus agreed. "I have heard him several times," he said, "and though he appears careless in his appearance and crude in his speech he has great power and influence with all types of people, but I fear that today he signed his own death warrant."

"You mean when he called the Pharisees a generation of vipers?"

Nicodemus laughed heartily. "Not at all!" he answered. "In fact sometimes I agree with him completely."

"Father!" Mariamne remonstrated, joining in the laughter. "You sound as if we should all be crawling around in the shrubs outside the door!"

"I assume then," Nicodemus continued, putting his arm around

Mariamne and turning toward me, "that your own sudden and unwilling baptism caused you to leave the riverside before John's stern denunciation of Herod for having taken his brother's wife in marriage. I am told that Herod rode away in high dudgeon, and that although there was much jeering and laughter, some of the poorer people were afraid to stay and listen after Herod left."

"I feel sorry for Herodias," Mariamne said. "The story is already going all over Jerusalem, and by the end of the week it will have reached Galilee and Herod's own town of Tiberias. The people there know that Herod and Salome and Herodias consider them uncultured and gauche, and you can be sure they will make the most of it."

"Waste no sympathy on her, my dear," Nicodemus said. "Save it for the preacher. Herodias will not rest until she has made him pay in full for her humiliation."

"But what harm could she do him, sir?"

"Lysias," Nicodemus answered me solemnly, "it is a black and ugly stain upon the integrity of our once proud land that the father of this Herod bequeathed to his son the ability to manipulate the imprisonment—even the death—of a completely innocent person without ever having it come into the courts."

"Would not the Roman procurator protect an innocent person?"

"Pilate looks upon our people with distaste—even with contempt —but he knows this is the best post he ever will be offered, and one dead Jew, more or less, means nothing to him as long as he is in the confidence of those who are in power in Jerusalem."

Mariamne's mother arose. "Shall we go into the dining room and with supper find a more pleasant subject?"

As soon as we were seated, our glasses of red pomegranate juice in our hands, Mariamne suggested, "Why not tell Tribune Lysias of the strange experience you had last night, Father?"

"Lysias," Nicodemus said, "it is about the young teacher Jesus of whom we have spoken many times. Yesterday was not a pleasant day for me. It was one of those days when everything seems to go wrong. One of those days which can reduce a fullgrown man to the rather shameful condition of wanting to take a very juvenile kick at the nearest article of furniture. When night came,

I decided that perhaps a walk in the evening air might quiet my jangled nerves.

"I always enjoy walking down by the Temple, and as I passed along the south wall, I saw that a man was sitting on the steps of one of the massive gates which descend from the Royal Porch. This is not an unusual sight in Jerusalem where there are so many beggars, but it is one which always leaves me with a feeling of distress, and I turned aside, going nearer to ask if he needed help."

Nicodemus paused and ran the fingers of his right hand back and forth across his forehead. "I fear that it may seem to you, Lysias, that what happened was attributable to the lights and shadows of the early evening on the steps of the great roofed gate, but the instant I came near enough to see the face of the person I meant to help, I knew that this man was no beggar. For one single, inexplicable moment I was persuaded that it was I who was the mendicant asking alms of him.

"I recalled some of the things which you and other of my friends have told me, and without hesitation, I said to him, 'You are Jesus!' and I sat down on the dusty steps beside him. I found no explanation for it then and I find none now, but it was exactly as if I sat beside him on a throne."

I interrupted Nicodemus to say quickly that I understood, that I had sensed that same dignity, that same kingly poise when I had seen him with a little whip in his hands driving birds and cattle and men out of the Temple court.

Nicodemus hardly seemed to notice what I had said, so intent was he upon his own memories of Jesus. "'Rabbi,' I said to him," he continued, "I know that you are a teacher sent from God!' and you could never imagine what answer he made!"

"He told my father that he must be born again," Mariamne joined in, excitement in her voice.

"And if you knew my husband as I do," Nicodemus' wife added, "you would suppose that he rose with great dignity and resentment and walked away."

"But I did not!" Nicodemus stated positively. "I sat there— just looking at him. His clothes were the clothes of a peasant.

You will not mind my saying so, Lysias, but like you, my background is an aristocratic one. My education, culture, and position are unexcelled in Palestine—perhaps in all the world. I am certain you understand that I recount these things only to show you how amazed I was at his statement."

"Indeed, sir! These things are well known to me. What do you think he meant about being born again?"

"I asked him what he meant. I, Nicodemus, asked with the eagerness a child might use in questioning a parent, and he used the same patience and the same simplicity in answering me that I might have used in explaining a difficult problem to a backward student!

"He told me that our God has sent his own son into the world to live here in a body like ours to try to show people what God is like, and that all those who will believe in him need not perish but shall have everlasting life!"

"It is not easy to comprehend, sir."

"It was not easy for me. It is not easy now. I have given it hours of thought, and very slowly I am beginning to discern that what Jesus wanted me to see is that the things in which we take such pride—wealth and position and education and culture—while they are good things and greatly to be desired, are as nothing before God."

"Both Mariamne and I have remembered," Mariamne's mother joined in, "things which one of our prophets wrote many years ago. Even then this Isaiah pictured God as saying, 'Bring me no more vain offerings; incense is an abomination to me . . . . Your new moons and your appointed feasts my soul hates; they have become a burden to me, I am weary of bearing them!' "

Nicodemus spoke slowly. "I think perhaps this is something our God has been trying for centuries to get into our small finite minds. I think that Jesus meant there is the need in every man—however moral, however replete with his own good works, however careful with his rites and ceremonies—to become like a newborn babe, willing to let God do for him something which he cannot possibly do for himself."

"Perhaps, sir," I answered. "I find your God most difficult to understand."

As I walked through the dark streets back to the tower, I thought to myself that I was beginning to discern what it was that set these Jewish people apart, what it was that made those of other countries consider them a peculiar people. It was, I thought, that this small land was permeated with religion.

I thought of Athens, filled with altars and temples and images, of beautiful statuary in marble, gold, silver, bronze, and wood, all evidences of man's wistful seeking for something to worship. These things, to my own family and to our friends, had always seemed only a need of the insecure, a solace for the downtrodden.

I remembered with a kind of warm glow the words of the poorly dressed woman with a tearstained face and with a pot of red soup in her hands as she spoke unabashedly of her God to a superior officer of the Roman army. "The Lord bless you, sir, and keep you," she had said. "The Lord make his face to shine upon you."

Suddenly I remembered the great statue in Athens with the inscription, "To the Unknown God," and I wondered if this might be the God of Nicodemus.

Perhaps it was not bad, I thought, this certainty about something greater than one's self.

On the following day I did not think about the Jewish religion.

I thought about Mariamne. I began to count the days which usually elapsed before Nicodemus repeated an invitation to his house. Perhaps, I told myself, now that he was not lonely, he would not invite me at all.

Not more than a week had gone by, however, before I was sitting again in the great vaulted reception room, and on this late afternoon it seemed to have taken on added beauty. The couches and chairs, fashioned of red bronze and covered with silken cushions, the intricate fretwork of the huge bronze door which led into the garden with its long line of slender pillars leading to a summerhouse, the graceful saffron draperies at the tall windows, all had a charm which I had somehow missed. From somewhere could be heard the strange, enchanting songs of the Jewish people, half sad, half gay, but always with an overtone of religion, sung by itinerant minstrels with accompaniments of a zither and a flute.

When it began to grow dark the servants came in and began

to light the tall bronze floor lamps. I looked at Mariamne. I wanted to know why I had thought of her so constantly. She was evidently several years my junior, and I could not have said she was beautiful. But there was something else. She was gay and shining, and yet for one so young, there was a deep serenity about her, as if already she knew where she was going, and why.

At the rear of the house Nicodemus had an unusual library containing scores of scrolls concerning not only the history, the prophecies, and the psalms which his own people had sung for centuries, but the histories of the Gallic War written by Julius Caesar, and of the wars between the Romans and the Numidian king Jugurtha, written by Sallust. Niches which covered three walls were filled with the works of Horace, the wittiest of the poets, and of the Greek lyric poet Alcaeus whom he imitated.

Not many people had the wealth or the incentive to possess such a library, and on that night friends came toward the middle of the evening wishing to examine some scrolls which Nicodemus had lately acquired of the great comic dramatist Aristophanes, of my own city of Athens.

Nicodemus and his wife went with the visitors, and I was left alone with Mariamne.

I, whose tongue, particularly when girls were concerned, had always been too glib for my own good, could think of nothing to say.

"You seem to like us, Tribune Lysias," Mariamne said with a smile.

"I do like you," I answered, solemn as an owl.

"Not everybody does," she said, as if it were not a matter of great moment. "Although our people are truly loved and chosen by our God, we are not always loved and chosen by our fellow-men."

I thought of how pleased my friend Julius would have been to hear this evidence of something less than complete self-satisfaction in a member of the race whose lack of respect for Roman strength and power he resented so heartily.

She walked to a table and refilled our glasses with a warm, sweet drink, and I thought again of how like Nicodemus she was in facing issues without bitterness or resentment. When she was seated she held her glass in her hand for a moment, looking at it, and when she spoke, the light touch, the gayety, was gone. She was solemn now, and in earnest.

"Perhaps we talk too much of our religion and of our God, Tribune Lysias, but we carry a heavy responsibility. Two thousand years ago God chose a man named Abraham out of a pagan land, saying to him, 'If you will leave your country and your kinsmen and go to a land which I will show you, I will make of you a great nation, a nation in which all the nations of the earth shall be blessed.' Abraham believed God, and we believe him too. We know that he does not fail, nor forget his promises."

Mariamne raised her great dark eyes to mine. "I do not know when it will be, but I am sure that from our race, in this tiny land of Palestine, something or someone will come to bless and to heal this whole great world with all its people."

During my student days I had been with many girls and had fancied myself in love with most of them. I had sought them out because I considered them attractive or beautiful or exciting. Not once had I heard any of them refer to such a matter as this young girl was discussing.

I looked at her with added interest. I saw that her eyes were shining, and a kind of a glow was on her face. I told myself that I had been mistaken in thinking Mariamne was not beautiful.

"I shall be saying farewell to you for a while, Tribune Lysias."

"You are going away?"

"To visit my friend, Susanna, daughter of Matthew of the city of Capernaum. We have been friends since we were little girls. My mother and father have a summer cottage on the beach near the great house of Matthew on the shore of the Sea of Galilee. Susanna and I have loved each other since the time when gathering sea shells was excitement enough to fill our days. I love her father too."

"Her mother?"

"Matthew's wife died when Susanna was born, and Matthew has taken the place of two parents instead of one. My father sometimes regrets Matthew's rather unethical practices in his business of tax-collecting, but I feel sure it is because Susanna has a congenital lameness which makes Matthew more eager to accumulate wealth than he might be otherwise. He never seems satisfied until Susanna has everything which I or any of the other girls in Capernaum or Jerusalem have."

I felt a definite sense of loss that Mariamne was leaving Jerusalem when she had so lately returned, as if somehow I was being cheated.

"When will you go?"

"Tomorrow morning, early."

"I shall miss you," I said, restraining a desire to touch her.

Tribune Julius was in a bad mood. I was sitting with Zoldi and the other tribunes on one of the parapets of the tower high above the city where, after the sun went down, a cool breeze blew in from across the Tyropoeon Valley. It was August, the summer had been hot, and tempers were on edge. Julius was not easy to take as he lashed out, first at one of us and then at the other.

"The beautiful Salome has arrived with her loving stepfather from Tiberias," one of the men said, tauntingly. "She is walking the streets of Jerusalem, and it makes the Roman Conqueror nervous. He fears the dust may touch the hem of her robe!"

"It is the great hero of the Jewish people—Tribune Claudius Lysias of Athens, Greece—who must not soil his feet upon the unworthy streets of the city," answered Julius. "Look, some day when the sun shines brightly, you may see on his heels the wings of Hermes or of Mercury. A messenger of the gods indeed!"

"Couldn't we just forget that small incident, Julius?" I asked with mounting irritation. "You were there. You know there was nothing heroic about it. I saw the boy in the deep water, and I jumped in. If I had had time to think I probably would not have moved from my tracks."

"Not according to the bowing, scraping population of Jerusalem!" Julius insisted. " 'The tribune was not dressed for swimming! The tribune might have lost his life! The river was deep and treacherous! The tribune is a brave and good man!' "

I tried to keep my mind on the words which Nicodemus had said to me the previous evening when I had discussed with him the trying and contradictory Julius.

"You must remember, my boy," he said, "that it is not usually the big things which determine a person's happiness in life. Human beings seem to have a surprising capacity for accepting disappointment or sorrow—even tragedy—with a measure of grace, but it is the small, sometimes irritating, concerns of simple, everyday living that can pull and tear until one's day or one's life is spoiled.

"A man of great wisdom put it well when he wrote that it is the little foxes that destroy the grapes. The young teacher Jesus has a more direct approach. 'Make friends quickly with your accuser,' he tells those who gather about him on the street corners. It is a fine premise, Lysias, if you will think about it. It not only leaves one's adversary confused and uncertain, but it gives to one who can follow his advice the decided advantage of a great inner calm."

Zoldi glanced at me, and at Julius. He began to speak of armor which might need polishing in case Tetrarch Herod should make an unexpected visit to the tower during his stay in Jerusalem. It was not long before he and the others climbed down from the parapet to their quarters.

Julius stayed. He put his hand on my arm as if to detain me. Hoping to change his critical mood, I asked him a question quickly. I had discovered, however, that he was one of those persons who seem to be pleasant enough when there are no others around, but who cannot resist holding a friend up to ridicule or censure in the company of others.

"Have you been back out to the wilderness to hear the preacher?" I asked.

"No," he replied. "Lately we have been going in the evenings when it is dark and listening to Jesus. He does not talk about chaff which will be cast into the fire or trees which will be dug up from the roots. He talks about the dignity of the individual and about people loving each other."

"You said 'we,' Julius. Do some of the other tribunes go with you?"

Julius rose abruptly. "Let's go to your room, Lysias," he said. "One never knows who may be sitting around on these parapets."

When we reached my quarters, Julius made another strange request. "Do not light the lamps," he said. "I have something I wish to say to you. Lysias, do you know what is being said on the streets of Jerusalem and what is believed up in the northern part of Palestine? There are increasing numbers of people who believe that Jesus is the one for whom—about thirty years ago— wise men came from eastern countries seeking, declaring him to be the newly-born king of the Jews. Salome says that every one of the Jewish prophecies has been fulfilled, the place of birth, the flight into Egypt—everything!"

Although I did not understand him fully, I was interested in what Julius was saying, but one name stood out in his remarks.

"Salome?" I asked, incredulously. "Surely you do not mean the beautiful girl whom I saw dancing at Pilate's supper party last April, the one to whom the tribune referred as we were talking on the parapet!"

My eyes had grown accustomed to the dimness of the room, and I could see the black look which settled on Julius' face. I saw, or sensed, that the knuckles were white on his clenched right hand. For a moment the atmosphere was so tense that I wondered if he was going to get up from his stool and strike me.

"They will tell you many things, Tribune," he said sternly. "They will tell you many things which are not true. It is always a bad time for me when Salome comes to Jerusalem. Salome's black hair and her black eyes, her skin like a magnolia blossom, and her beautifully formed body, give her a smouldering look. She is not smouldering. She is sweet and gentle and afraid. It is her ruthless, ambitious mother who demands that she dance the lewd dances and that she accept in public the beastly attentions of her stepfather so that Herodias may ask more and more favors for herself."

"Salome goes with you to listen to Jesus?"

"She begs me many times to leave our secret meeting place and go with her to stand in the dark and listen to him."

"Are you not jealous?"

"Jealous?" he repeated.

"Is not this Jesus a man?"

"He is a man—and more—" Julius answered with conviction, "but one is not jealous of him."

When Julius—strange champion of the Roman Empire, strange hater of the Jewish race—had gone, I walked down the corridor to Zoldi's apartment. I was completely baffled.

Zoldi shook his head, and thought for a moment before he answered my question. "The other tribunes dislike Julius so heartily, Lysias," he said, "that I think they wait almost with bated breath for the day when he discovers for himself that his Salome is a siren, as insidious and deceptive as any who ever lured a mariner to his watery grave. It is well known from Galilee to Judea, even among the common soldiers, that she takes her male companionship where she finds it. Any reference to this, however, any lift of the eyebrows when Salome is mentioned, throws Julius into a raging temper."

"Why do you suppose Salome adopts this strange role of a sweet and innocent girl dominated by her mother?"

"I do not know. It may be that she cannot resist using any means she finds available to draw into her power every man with whom she comes in contact. There is also the possibility that she is influenced by his position and that Julius has an unlimited amount of money at his disposal. A high officer in the Roman army who can supply the luxuries which she may find it difficult to extract from the self-centered Herodias, may well discount the boredom she almost surely feels when she is alone with him. It also may be a rather novel and gratifying experience to find herself placed on a pedestal and worshiped as a virgin in distress."

"Do you suppose Salome actually believes these stories which are being circulated about Jesus?"

"No person can look into another person's heart, Lysias. It would be my opinion, however, that Salome has heard the Jewish prophecies all her life, and while she may see the possibility that they are fulfilled in Jesus, her insistence on hearing him is really because it relieves her of spending time with Julius after she has accomplished her purpose of obtaining money for herself."

"Poor Julius!" I said. "I suppose no good ever can come of it."

"No good ever can come of it," Zoldi answered. "Poor Julius!"

Lunch With Pontius Pilate

The following day Julius and his problems were dismissed from my mind. I received a summons from Pontius Pilate to appear in his chambers at the hour of noon. I had seen the Roman procurator only the one time, and remembering how he had impressed me as one eager to feel important, I dreaded the interview. I had found it true that nothing can be more trying than a person set upon being important.

As I entered a private sitting room, Pilate was reclining on a massive ivory couch, his head propped up with silken cushions. He was wearing a short, oblong mantle fastened with a single clasp at the shoulder, similar to the Greek chalmys, and the absence of the purple and gold toga, the gilded sandals, and even the great gold and amethyst ring, gave me courage.

"Be seated, Tribune Lysias," he said cordially. "I can imagine that you have felt some wonder, perhaps apprehension, at being called here before me today."

I made an intense effort to adopt the same casual and easy manner he was using. "Yes, Governor," I replied, "ever since I received your summons, I have felt much as I did in the early days of my schooling when I was told to report to the office of the head-master."

Pilate laughed heartily, and I felt that my addressing him as governor instead of as procurator had been a lucky stroke on my part. I was grateful he did not know that it had been a slip of the tongue rather than any mistake as to his actual position in Palestine. His manner was so pleasant and so much in contrast with what I had expected that after a few minutes I began to wonder if he might have elements of kindness and consideration which I had not suspected.

"Tribune Lysias," he said, suddenly becoming quite business-like, "you did a splendid thing in establishing a better relationship between the people of Palestine and the Roman army. I refer to the fact that you risked your life to save a Jewish child. These Jews are an emotional people, and they love their children. We could have marched our entire Roman legion through the streets of every city and village of Palestine, and we would have stirred nothing but added hatred and resentment toward us, but this is something which is understood by everybody. You are loved in Palestine, Tribune, and that is something which has been accomplished by few Gentiles, and I doubt if ever by a member of the Roman army."

"I am embarrassed, sir. I assure you it was not as great a deed as the people seem to think."

"It was a good deed, Tribune," Pilate declared. "I have had your behavior observed by one of the common soldiers whom I keep on constant watch in the Tower Antonia for that purpose, and you have passed all my requirements as to ability, integrity, and exemplary behavior with your fellow officers. I can anticipate that you will some day be placed in full charge of the Jerusalem garrison if you can tolerate these Jews for a long enough period."

"I feel sure that any such outcome would require added time and qualifications, sir," I answered. "As to being able to tolerate the Jews, however, I do not find the task as distasteful as I had anticipated. My parents and I resented my being sent to this post among people whose customs and traditions were so different from our own, but I have formed some friendships among the Jewish citizens which I value highly."

"I know, Tribune. Your friendship with Nicodemus is one of your greatest assets in my eyes. He is not one to be impressed by pomp or power, and for a man of his standing to have sought your friendship and to have invited you to his house is of inestimable value to the entire Roman-Jewish relationship."

"I had not thought of it in that light at all, sir. We have many things in common, and our mutual interest in a young teacher named Jesus has heightened our interest in each other."

"Jesus!" Pilate exclaimed, getting up and walking over to the window. "Everywhere I turn in the last few weeks I seem to hear his name mentioned. I never have seen him, but if I do, I shall offer him official thanks. He has been giving these sanctimonious Pharisees a hard time!"

"I have seen him only briefly, but one thing I can tell you, sir, if you ever meet him, you will not forget him."

Pilate walked back to the couch, and pushed the cushions behind his head. There was a strange look on his face. It was as if a dark shadow had fallen across it, as if he was trying to rid himself of some sudden, undefined, feeling of fear or of dread.

He shrugged his shoulders slightly and continued, "I called you here, Tribune, to tell you of an assignment which you are to undertake for me. It concerns a regrettable custom of the Roman government which keeps the people of Palestine in a constant state of indignation against us. I shall want you to leave Jerusalem early tomorrow morning."

Either purposely to keep me in a state of suspense, or in conformance with a fixed custom, he clapped his hands, and an aide came into the room bearing a great silver tray with silver goblets of wine, silver dishes of sliced roast calf, huge dates and figs, and generous portions of red melon. For a time I forgot my intense interest in what Pilate had been saying.

When the tray had been removed, Pilate began to speak slowly. He held his silver goblet of wine, turned it round and round in his hands, and occasionally raised it to his lips.

"It is possible, Tribune, that you consider me a fortunate man. You look at me and think you see a man who has few problems. Perhaps you envy me a bit. Perhaps you think that I am one of those mortals who is favored by the gods. I tell you I am not! I am a man surrounded and entrapped by hatred and borne down by suspicion. These natives here in Palestine hate me. They hate me because I am a Gentile, because I am a pagan, not bowing down to their almighty God, and they hate me most because I am a Roman.

"I am not sure how well you understand this, Tribune, but these Jews, as no other nation in the world, have a system of politics which is so interwoven with their religion that there is no separating them. Their very laws were given to them by their God. Their High Priest is the president of their Supreme Court, and their lawyers are largely the scribes who copy and interpret their Scriptures. Their highest civic official, Herod the Tetrarch, who is as unorthodox a Jew as one can find, has his own private grudge against me. In the northern province, where he is ruler, the people are unusually excitable and turbulent. They all come trooping down to Jerusalem several times a year on their feast days, but it is during the Passover celebration that they are most unruly.

"It was during my first Passover season that a particularly jubilant group of Galileans who had lingered too long over their wine cups, were going into the Temple to make their sacrifices, and because one of the more obstreperous was arrested by the Temple guard, the entire crowd began to engage in a fight which was open to anyone. I was staying next door at the tower, and I ordered the whole group arrested. Those Galileans are strong, however, and they are fighters, therefore much blood was spilled. Herod has never forgiven me for what he terms my summary manner of dealing with subjects whom he considers exclusively under his jurisdiction. To this day he and all the Jews speak mournfully of the poor Galileans whose blood I caused to be mingled with their sacrifices."

"I can see, sir, that yours is not an enviable position."

"It is not." Pilate said, emphatically. "Except for the fact that the ambition of my wife for my political advancement is like a whip across my back, I should much prefer being a common soldier. In addition to the animosity which is felt for me in Palestine, I know I am watched constantly by paid henchmen of Vitellius of Syria who is my immediate superior. To try to please Vitellius and a multitude of Jews at the same time is something no man can accomplish."

Pilate had slumped forward on his couch, and sat with his hands clasped loosely together and hanging between his knees. His whole attitude betokened a man torn and harassed by a position too big for him. Suddenly he straightened his shoulders, and raised his right hand authoritatively. I remembered the gold and amethyst ring.

"Now as I was saying," he went on, as if there had been no interruption, "one of the chief causes of unrest among the Jews is the heavy tax which they are required to pay to the Roman government. I must concede that in many parts of Palestine there is justification for their continued complaining. The tax itself is not exorbitant, but the method of collecting it is completely reprehensible."

"What method is used, sir?" I asked.

"I was about to explain," he said, and I was certain from the tone of his voice that he did not wish to be interrupted. I was there to listen, not to make conversation.

"Instead of having regularly appointed revenue officers, whose duty it would be to collect a fixed tax, Tiberius demands that at regular intervals I hold a sort of auction. The bidding is done by men of great wealth, most of whom have made fortunes in this field. Occasionally there are bidders among the Roman soldiers of equestrian rank or higher, but they have small chance in competition with the Jews. After the bidding is finished, men who will do the actual work of collecting in the different districts pay to the original bidders huge sums for the privilege of holding the office of tax-collector or publican, as they are called. These Jews are hated by their own people. The great wealth most of them have amassed proves that they are more nearly described as extortioners than as civic officials. A fixed sum must be paid to Rome, but whatever can be added is strictly up to the publicans. It has been called to my attention that the infinitesimal things which are being taxed is getting beyond all reason.

"Tomorrow, Tribune Lysias, I wish you to begin an extended tour of investigation. I plan to have you travel as far north as Capernaum in Galilee. I have had a detailed itinerary prepared, and I wish you to follow it exactly. First, you are to spend a few days at the home of Martha in the village of Bethany. As you know, perhaps, Bethany is only about two miles from Jerusalem across the Mount of Olives. There is no publican there, but I wish it to appear that you are preparing an article to be sent to Greece concerning the customs, beliefs, agricultural products, and manufactured articles of Palestine. These Jews are not slow of wit, and if it should be noised abroad that a tribune had spent several hours with me and then had begun to visit the office of tax-collectors, before you could reach your first assignment in Jericho, only seventeen miles away, every shred of evidence as to unethical behavior would have been concealed. If your conscience troubles you, you may actually prepare such an article. Time often will hang heavy on your hands."

"This Martha—does she have an inn?"

"No, she has a large house, and gives lodging to travelers. I am told by those who have spent time in her house that it is immaculate, her linens glistening white, and that her date pudding compensates for her taciturnity of manner."

Pilate rose to his full height, stood stiffly as if at attention. "I suggest that you return to your barracks now," he said, "and make preparations for your journey."

I walked toward the tower and was at a loss to understand the sense of excitement and of exhilaration which I was feeling toward this journey. Travel in Palestine was far from being the pleasant experience it was in Greece or in Italy. The roads were bad and often dangerous. Certainly the mission itself portended more of unpleasantness than of enjoyment. Yet I was feeling the warm sense of anticipation which one experiences when returning to a place well-known and loved.

I searched my mind for the answer, and I began to remember one small bit of conversation. Conversation with a girl whose shining eyes and glowing face, as she spoke of her responsibility to her God, had made her seem more beautiful than I had thought. "I shall have to bid you farewell," she had said. "I am going for a visit to my friend Susanna in Capernaum of Galilee."

I knew the strange, small glow of excitement was because I was glad I was going to see Mariamne again.

Simple Supper in Bethany

It was almost time for the evening meal, when after only a few inquiries on the streets of Bethany, I came easily to Martha's house. I saw at once that Pilate had been misinformed about its being a large house. It was actually quite small, and I wondered as I waited to be admitted if several days in such close proximity to the rather unpleasant woman Pilate had pictured might be a high price to pay for the fresh vegetables and the date puddings.

When the door opened, I could scarcely restrain a gasp of surprise. I suppose I had expected a woman with straggly gray hair and a sullen expression, but this girl was petite and lovely, with that freshly scrubbed look which some girls seem to have and others never seem able to achieve.

"I am Claudius Lysias, tribune in the Roman army," I said. "I have a room engaged for me by his honor, Pontius Pilate."

"Please come inside, Tribune Lysias," the girl said cordially, "we have been expecting you. I am Mary, and my sister Martha is finishing the preparations for the evening meal. This," moving a slender hand toward a tall boy who had walked up behind her, "is our brother Lazarus."

A door opened from the back of the room, and a woman entered. I decided at once that this must be Martha, although a very different Martha from the one Pilate's few words concerning her had led me to expect. While she was not young, as her sister Mary was young, nor pretty with Mary's fresh prettiness, she was far from being either old or unattractive. I could see that the deep lines around her mouth and at the corners of her eyes might be mistaken for unfriendliness but that they were more probably the result of constant fatigue and uneasiness.

"I am Martha," she said, "and my sister and my brother and I have been waiting to tell you that we feel it an honor to have you in our home. Bethany is so near to Jerusalem that it was only an hour or two after you saved the little boy from the river that we heard of it here. We called your name, sir, in our evening prayer. You are a good man."

She seemed to sense my discomfort, and she added quickly, "Supper will be ready in a few minutes, and in the meantime Lazarus will show you to your room so that you may refresh yourself before we eat."

Lazarus led the way up a steep flight of stairs to the one room which was not on the ground floor. I could see that though Pilate had been mistaken about the size of the house and about Martha's disposition, he had not been mistaken about her meticulous house-keeping. The room was small and sparsely furnished. The couch was narrow, but the hand-woven coverlet was sparkling in its cleanliness.

I looked out the small, high window, and I could see a grove of fig trees and a thriving vegetable garden. I saw a patch of rue with its bluish-green leaves and yellow flowers such as I had seen on my way from Joppa. I sniffed the evening air, and although I still enjoyed the strong sweet odor, I remembered that Zoldi had told me the leaves were used for medicine. The upper room was above the general level of the roof, and there were on the roof, figs and dates and several varieties of root vegetables.

"A nice view," I said to Lazarus.

"It means more than a view to us, sir," he answered, coming to stand beside me. "The figs and dates and vegetables, even the rue, have meant food and warmth to my sisters and me for as long as I can remember. Martha was only about twelve when our parents were killed. She became father, mother, and elder sister, as well as family bread-winner almost over night."

"It must have been a great responsibility for so small a girl."

"She worked, Tribune. She has always worked. She is always up before dawn, planting, weeding, hoeing in the groves and in the garden like a man. Every day in all kinds of weather she has pushed a vegetable and fruit cart across the mountain roads to Jerusalem to sell to the street merchants there. She crushes the leaves of the rue plants and makes them into medicine which she sells to the people of Bethany. When the people are poor and cannot afford to pay, she gives it to them."

Mary appeared at the door. "Supper is ready," she said.

I had eaten many fine meals with Nicodemus. I had enjoyed the exotic fruits and melons served at Pilate's lunch. But as I sat with Martha, Mary, and Lazarus and their elderly uncle who seemed to be a part of the household, I thought I had never tasted a more delicious supper.

There was no meat, but there was a thick red soup made of lentils, and my mind went back to the tear-stained face of Hannah standing at the foot of the tower stairs in Jerusalem. There were steaming hot cakes made from ground cereal and cooked on the hearth while we ate. There was butter to spread upon them, and wild honey with a taste like nuts. I asked Martha about the unusual butter, and she told me it was made by putting milk into a bottle made of skins, shaking and kneading it, and boiling it and putting it into pots. In mid-winter, she said, it was like candied honey. Pilate's report of the date pudding had not been exaggerated.

On my fourth day in Bethany I found myself regretting that I must leave for Jericho on the following morning. It crossed my mind that if I had needed to be repaid for saving young Caleb, the evident confidence and respect it had inspired in this small Jewish family had more than settled the debt.

We sat together, Martha and Mary and Lazarus and I, on the tiny but beautiful court which was on the west side of the house. The day's work was ended and they were spent from their labors.

Lazarus flung himself down upon the grass with his arms spread wide, gazing up at the stars.

"Would you find it hard to believe, Tribune Lysias," he asked, "if I should tell you there was a time when I refused to help my sisters at all?"

Martha spoke reprovingly. "Lazarus!" she said. "It was not his fault, sir. It was only that he was growing too fast. Look how tall he is, as tall as you, and he is only eighteen."

"He was lazy!" said Mary with a laugh. "Just plain lazy!"

"I was lazy," Lazarus agreed, "and cynical, and disbelieving.

I made fun of Martha because she insisted on walking across the mountain to the Temple in Jerusalem on the sabbath day. I was confused and erratic but the worst part of it was that I considered myself perfect. I thought that Martha was a stupid and old-fashioned prig and Mary a necessary annoyance!"

"He is exaggerating, Tribune," Martha told me. "And Lazarus is so changed since the first time Jesus came to our house that there is no need for us ever to speak of those things again."

"Jesus?" I asked. "Is this the same Jesus who has been teaching in Jerusalem? I saw him one time in the Temple, and my friend Nicodemus has had one small interview with him, but we both were much interested in him."

Lazarus sat upright. "Do you mean to tell me," he asked, "that the great Nicodemus, a Jew, a member of the Sanhedrin, would be friends with a Gentile, a Roman soldier?"

"My child," Martha remonstrated, "you must be more respectful!"

"But I have always heard," Lazarus insisted, "that the rich and influential Jews in Jerusalem have no dealings with members of the Roman army, and that the soldiers spend no time grieving about it."

"It is not true, Lazarus," I told him. "Nicodemus and his family are my valued friends. I am sure they feel as I do, that it is not a person's ancestry which determines his worth but the things which are in his heart and mind. But tell me about this Jesus and how he came to make such a change in you as Martha says."

Martha rose from her chair a little stiffly and put her hand on Mary's shoulder. "You must excuse my sister and me, Tribune," she said. "We are not used to late hours. Since this is your last night with us I do not wish to deprive my brother of the pleasure of further conversation, but do not let him keep you too long.

"We Jews do not break our fast until nine o'clock, but Mary and I will be astir early and will prepare you a hot breakfast. Lazarus will go with you a short distance to see that you are on the right road."

She came over to me, and touched my arm lightly. "The roads from here to Jericho are very dangerous, sir," she said. "I shall pray that God will go with you."

"Good night, Martha," I answered. "I shall be sorry to leave."

Lazarus left his place on the grass, and we sat together on the bench which Mary had occupied.

"Tell me about your meeting with Jesus," I reminded him.

"I wish to tell you, sir," he said. "It was about this time in the evening when he first came to our house. We were late in eating our evening meal because Martha had not returned from her regular trip into the city with the fruits and vegetables.

"Mary was worried. 'Talk about something else!' I told her. 'Martha is not pretty enough for any man to run away with her.' Mary answered tartly. 'You do not know what pretty is!' she said, 'except those flibberty-gibbets I see you with in the village!'

"It was funny about Mary and me, Tribune. Since I was five and she seven, our small fights have always started the same way. Remarks getting sharper and louder, then accompanied by a small shove, then a real push, and then the battle royal! Age has never seemed to make a difference.

"It was while such a battle was going on that night, Mary running around the table squealing, and I in hot pursuit, that the door opened and Martha came in, followed by a tall young man."

"It was Jesus?"

"It was Jesus. Ordinarily I would have thought to myself that perhaps I was mistaken, that perhaps my elder sister was prettier than I had supposed. But no such thought came into my mind. There was friendliness in this young man who entered, and under-standing—even for the silly scene he had witnessed—but there was dignity, and something which I could not define. Immediately I hoped he was going to stay for supper.

" 'This is Jesus,' Martha said to Mary and me. 'A sudden wind in the city upset my cart and scattered my produce. Jesus helped me.' "

Lazarus stood up, and began to walk about the court. "That was the thing which set him apart, Tribune. I could not tell how I had come upon the knowledge, but I knew that whatever the situation, this man would give help.

"Both Mary and I felt a sudden disinterest in our small battle. We were ashamed, and something I never had felt before was stir-ring in my heart because this kindly, uncritical man had seen my elder sister struggling with a produce cart on the streets of Jerusalem while I, a great hulking boy, found nothing more useful to do than chase my other sister around the supper table. Suddenly, in his presence, I felt immature, and gauche, and useless."

Lazarus sat down again beside me. "After my sisters had retired, we sat here that night, Tribune, Jesus and I, just as you and I sit now. He put his hand on my arm and said, 'What was it you wished to ask me, Lazarus?'

"'I do not know, sir, what it is I wish to ask,' I told him. And then, Tribune, the words seemed fairly to tumble from my lips. I told him I did not know why it was I always spoke with such condescension to my sister Martha when I loved her so, why it was that when she said the evening prayer, I would not bow my head, and made sure she saw that I would not. I told him I did not know why I always wanted to strike out at Mary, but did not really want to hurt her. I told him how it was that on one day I wanted to finish my education as Martha wished to have me finish it, and on the next to become a street merchant, and on the next to be a wanderer in foreign lands."

Lazarus walked to the edge of the court, kicked at a bit of loose turf, and then continued hesitantly, "You are not a Jew, Tribune. Perhaps you can understand if I tell you what I said to him. I said, 'Martha thinks our God will help me to decide, but I do not know if there is a God!'"

"Being a teacher of the Jewish religion, he rebuked you, Lazarus, I am sure."

"He did not. He told me a story, and then he went upstairs to his bed. I listened so carefully and have thought of it so often that I can repeat it almost word for word.

"It was about a boy like me who rebelled against his father's authority. He took his part of the inheritance and went into a far country and spent it all. He even had to get a job feeding hogs and would have eaten the garbage if he had dared. He thought of the food his father gave the hired servants. He decided to go home and ask to be a servant himself.

"I knew that Jesus was telling me about God. 'While the boy was yet afar off,' he said, 'his father saw him, and ran down the road to meet him. He gave him a robe and shoes and a ring for his finger. He put his arms around him and kissed him, and told the servants to kill the fatted calf, and told them all, This is my son who was lost, and now is found.' "

I was to hear this story which Lazarus was telling more than two years later as Jesus told it to a great multitude, and was to wonder how many times he had told it, and how many people had seen themselves as this young boy saw himself—the son who had been lost and now was found.

"Jesus always stays with us whenever he is in this part of Palestine," Lazarus continued. "To Martha he is like an elder brother, to me he is like a father, but to Mary he is God."

Even I, Claudius Lysias, a Greek with a god in every treetop, felt a small sense of shock. I knew how reverent the Jewish people were, how high and holy they believed their God to be, and I was not prepared for such a statement from a young man of Jewish ancestry.

"Mary loves the Jewish prophecies," Lazarus explained. "An old scribe lives nearby, and Mary will sit for hours as he reads. Tribune Lysias, all Jews believe that God will one day send a strong and mighty deliverer who will establish a Jewish world empire. Our Mary makes up her own mind.

"She says that our God will one day take upon himself a body like ours—subject to pain and loneliness and death—so that he can understand fully and be touched by the feeling of human infirmities. She quotes the prophet Isaiah who wrote, 'He was despised and rejected of men, a man of sorrows and acquainted with grief.'

"You ought to see the look on her face when Jesus is talking and she sits at his feet. It is the look of a priestess worshiping her God!"

"And what of Martha, is she in sympathy with Mary's belief?"

"She is not. Sometimes when Jesus is here, she has to call Mary many times to perform her share of the work."

"And you, Lazarus?"

"I am waiting."

Unwelcome Guest in Jericho

Except to the wealthy Jews who traveled extensively, the solidly constructed highways which were in the other parts of the empire—planned and executed by Roman engineering genius—were beyond the imagination. As I rode along the rocky, twisting road toward Jericho, marked out only by the regular travel upon it, I thought of the excellent roads in Greece and of the beautiful Appian Way on the western coast of Italy leading from the southern port of Brundisium to the city of Rome. I remembered Martha's words about the dangers on this journey from Bethany to Jericho and her wish that her God would protect me. I smiled to myself and thought that if Martha asked him, I did not see how he could refuse.

I was relieved, however, when finally I came into view of the city as it lay in the valley of the Jordan River at the foot of the ascent to the mountainous tableland of Judah. Lying as it did, many hundred feet below the level of the Mediterranean Sea, Jericho was a tropical paradise. Palm trees and luxuriant balsams and sycamores and henna trees flourished along the sides of all the roads. Great rose bushes were in bloom in the courts and occasionally in small cultivated areas in the midst of the commercial districts. There was a huge old palace in a place of prominence, a showy, ornate hippodrome, and a citadel on the hill behind the town.

As I came into the principal business section, I was approached by a small group of men who had the look and airs of an important delegation. They stopped directly in front of me, and one of them, with a sweeping bow, spoke.

"Welcome to our city, Tribune Claudius Lysias! Our master,

Zacchaeus, collector of taxes for the Roman government, invites you to be his guest while you are in Jericho."

Something had gone wrong with Pilate's plans. If this publican whose activities I was to investigate was prepared for my arrival, I must make the best of it. I was not capable of answering in the grand manner in which I had been greeted, but I did my best, and went with the deputation to the house of Zacchaeus. When I saw the elegance of the quadrangular mansion surrounding a formal court, I decided that if wealth was the criterion, Zacchaeus must be the most adept of all the publicans in placing a tax on the inconsequential things about which Pilate had told me.

Sitting in my large bedroom until the afternoon turned into twilight, I began to wonder if the great Zacchaeus and his elaborately dressed servants had forgotten me. A knock at the door, and the same impressive man with the same impressive bow, said to me, "The evening meal is now being served in the gold room."

I was now so mystified that if I had been ushered into a room actually decorated with pure gold, I could not have felt less comfortable. Standing rigidly at the door of the ornate "gold room," was the smallest man I had ever seen. He stood as if he were a general about to deliver an order, or perhaps like royalty about to receive his lowliest servant.

"Be seated," he said, bowing slightly and looking straight ahead. Beads of perspiration were beginning to gather on my forehead, but I felt sure there must be icicles clinging to the back of my neck. I never could have believed a man could convey such coldness in two innocuous words.

The food, which must have been in keeping with the surrounding pomp and circumstance, was like ashes in my mouth. Zacchaeus began at once to carry on a running report of his houses, his lands, his position of high responsibility with the Roman government, and his close friendship with all the important personages in both Palestine and Rome. My mind wandered, but the conclusion of one sentence brought me quickly to attention " . . . have heard of the articles you are writing concerning the eminent citizens of Palestine, and I felt sure you would want to stay in my house."

I drew a deep breath of relief. This egocentric little man did not know of my real mission in Jericho. "You must not be misled, Tribune," he continued, "about the Jewish people. If you have visited in the small village of Bethany with people who were poor and without the things of culture, you must remember that they are not representative of the best. You must understand also that the fanatical beliefs which they probably hold concerning one God, or the hope of a coming Messiah, are not beliefs to which the educated Jews subscribe. Now I," he said, straightening up on his cushioned bench, and adjusting his ornate robe at the shoulders, "I have long since taken up the worship of the gods and goddesses of the Romans and of your own people. I want you to see the intricately designed shelf which I have filled with beautiful gold and ivory carvings of Jupiter, Zeus, and Diana."

My mind wandered again as Zacchaeus began to recount in great detail his journeys into Italy and Greece and Egypt, but again one sentence drew my attention. This, I realized, concerned the very business for which I had been sent to Jericho. " . . . no sympathy for these whining, sniveling swine who want a reduction in their taxes."

"The people here object to paying their lawful tax to the Roman government?" I asked.

"Object!" he repeated with bitterness in his voice. "Object! Object! Object! That is all they do! You ought to hear the fantastic tales they bring me! Only this morning, a man who lives down in the slum district in the river bottoms, came here with some fanciful story about a sick wife and six or seven children who were crying for food. He prostrated himself on the ground before me, begging me to go down into that slimy, filthy section to see how the people live. He sickened me. I felt an almost uncontrollable desire to kick him. Can you imagine, Tribune Lysias, his wanting a representative of Tiberius Caesar to go to such a place?"

I might have told this little man that the sickness he had felt would not compare with the emotion I was feeling, nor perhaps would the almost uncontrollable desire for a well-placed kick.

"There is really such a section in this beautiful city?" I asked him, with what calm I could command.

"Certainly there is!" he answered, "there is such a section in every city! You cannot change these lazy, shiftless beggars! If you should give them all the same amount of money as that possessed by the wealthy and important citizens, in less than a year they would all be back in the river bottoms. And besides, Tribune," he added, with a noble air, "you destroy their initiative once you start helping them. You would never again be rid of the responsibility of taking care of them and of their families."

"What would be your opinion as to the best way to solve this problem?" I asked him.

He laid the fruit he was paring on a silver dish, and began to pound on the edge of the table with his knife. "Keep them down!" he said vehemently. "Let them understand that every time they come here complaining, their taxes are going to be increased instead of lessened!" He smiled slyly, and I thought of something Nicodemus had read to me from his prophet Jeremiah who compared the amasser of great wealth to the partridge of his time which was believed to gather young which it had not brought forth and to sit upon eggs which it had not laid.

"Often when I cannot sleep," Zacchaeus was saying, "I amuse myself by compiling new lists of things I can tax."

He rubbed his hands together, gloatingly, until one could almost imagine gold coins dripping from his greedy, grasping fingers.

"I should like to see one of your lists, sir."

Zacchaeus gave me a quick look, and I realized this little Jew was as crafty and as perceptive as he was cruel and grasping. He arose from the table abruptly. "It is growing late," he said. "Tomorrow, if you wish, I will show you my Greek and Roman gods."

"I shall be leaving early."

"Then farewell," he said, and walked from the room.

It was just beginning to dawn the next morning when, without benefit of host or servants, I left Zacchaeus' house. The moon still hung palely in the sky, but the sun was sending up long spears of gold and crimson over the beautiful city with its palms and its roses, its palace and hippodrome and citadel.

But I was looking over to the east where, only five miles away, the Jordan River flowed. I was picturing a desperate man, with a sick wife and hungry children, trying to find the money to pay an exorbitant tax to an ugly, scheming, little Jew who would buy more gods of gold and ivory to set upon a shelf.

Midnight Supper on the Sea

The route which Pilate had mapped out for me showed his ability for fine strategy. Since he had wished to keep the reason for my journey secret, he had gone to great pains to direct my itinerary to numerous towns and cities where there was no publican, as well as to those in which he desired an investigation to be made. Often he had arranged for me to spend a few days, occasionally even a week, visiting the important citizens, inspecting the agricultural areas, and making well-publicized tours through the manufacturing plants where their household furniture was made, always, of course, with my notes in evidence.

Deeper than my concern with their wheat and barley, their figs and root vegetables, their really remarkable ability in craftsmanship, was my ever increasing interest in the religious attitude of these people. Their lives, and all they did and planned, seemed dominated by the conviction that their God was constantly aware of their simplest needs, their most mundane affairs.

The deities with whom I had been familiar since my childhood had been the multitudinous gods and goddesses of my own people —this one for war, that for love, this for the sea, that for the sky. It was possible, I thought, that there were Greeks who believed that these far-distant gods heard their petitions, and that they might be persuaded to relinquish their drinking of nectar and eating of ambrosia on Mount Olympus to straighten out the affairs of mere mortals, but I never had heard anyone picture them as being concerned with love or mercy or with tender understanding of human frailties.

It was amazing to me to find the most illiterate provincials able to stop in the midst of their plowing or their threshing, and as

they discussed the crops, the water supply, the welfare of their
horses and farmyard animals, quote long excerpts from the writings of their ancient prophets in words which fell from their lips
like the classic prose of our Greek historian Herodotus, or with
the fire and beauty of our tragic poets Sophocles or Euripides.

One old man, knowing I was a Greek, stood with his long white
beard blowing in the breeze, his hand on his plow, and denounced,
in the words of the Jewish prophet Isaiah, all idol worship—its
futility, its emptiness, its caricature of reality—and the words were
those of exquisite irony, as well as of the most profound reasoning
and logic.

"Listen, my son," he said. "Hear the words of our God as he
gave them to his messenger hundreds of years ago.

> " 'To whom will you liken me and make me equal,
>   and compare me, that we may be alike?
> Those who lavish gold from the purse,
>   and weigh out silver in the scales,
> hire a goldsmith, and he makes it into a god;
>   then they fall down and worship!
> They lift it upon their shoulders, they carry it,
>   they set it in its place, and it stands there;
>   it cannot move from its place.
> If one cries to it, it does not answer
>   or save him from his trouble. . . . ' "

"Those words concern the gods of the wealthy, my son," he
continued, "but the poor have idols too which are just as helpless
and equally as foolish. Listen again to Isaiah, as he spoke with
the words of God to those who could not afford to possess idols
made of gold or silver.

" 'He cuts down cedars; or he chooses a holm tree or an oak
and lets it grow strong among the trees of the forest; he plants a
cedar and the rain nourishes it. Then it becomes fuel for a man;
he takes a part of it and warms himself, he kindles a fire and
bakes bread; also he makes a god and worships it, he makes it a
graven image and falls down before it . . . he prays to it and says,
"Deliver me, for thou art my god!" ' "

As this old man recited the words of Scripture with such contempt in his voice and with such deep conviction, my thoughts turned to Zacchaeus back in Jericho, with his gods of ivory sitting on a shelf, and he himself bumping his forehead on the ground before them, saying, "Deliver me, oh, my gods of money and of position!" As I listened, the scorn of the old man was beginning to become my scorn, and I began to wonder how my people, considering themselves so superior in education and in cultural attainments, could have been so stupid in their choice of gods.

"I am the Lord! That is my name, and my glory I will not give to another, neither my praise to graven images."

The old farmer quoted these words with his head lifted high, and the Greek Fates who once had impressed me vaguely, as they pursued and hounded Aeschylus, now seemed no more reasonable or worthy of respect than the oak tree, with half of it used to bake bread and to roast meat, and the other half used to fashion a god in whom one hoped to find help in the time of stress.

+   +   +

After I had left the province of Peraea, according to Pilate's directions, I made my way northward into the region of Decapolis. Here I began to feel as if I had returned to my home in Athens, or at least to my own province of Achaia.

This district was dominated by ten Greek cities which had been built by Alexander the Great. They were situated strategically on the three main highways which connected the Plains of Esdraelon with the important commercial highway which led along the edge of the desert, south from Damascus, to Arabia.

The dominant features in all these cities were Grecian, and there seemed to be not only a geographical boundary but a definite cultural borderland. The population, with the exception of Damascus in Syria, was predominantly Jewish, but here one found the greatest infiltration of Hellenistic customs and beliefs of any part of Palestine. Often I saw great herds of hogs being driven through the main streets, while in most sections of Palestine the orthodox Jews would have lifted their hands in horror at such contamination.

It was late in the afternoon when I stabled my horse in the city of Gadara, the last of the towns I was to visit in Decapolis. As soon as I had settled myself in the dreary little inn where Pilate had made a reservation for me, and had partaken of a meal as dreary as the inn itself, I decided I would ride out to the seashore to try to engage passage on the first available boat going across the sea to the city of Capernaum.

Standing on the shore of this body of water which was called the Sea of Galilee, I found it difficult to believe that the warning which Pilate had included in his instructions could have been necessary. It was more of a lake than a sea since its waters were fresh, and it was only about thirteen miles long and six or seven miles wide. The waters looked so calm and blue in the late afternoon sunshine, with the shadows from the surrounding hills dancing across it, that his admonition to be certain that the boat upon which I engaged passage was of sturdy build, thoroughly sea-worthy, and able to withstand the sudden and violent storms to which this serene-looking water was subject, seemed almost unbelievable.

The innkeeper, while not a person to indulge in idle chatter or to furnish anything in the way of sparkling conversation along with his dreary rooms and meals, had waxed enthusiastic when, in answer to my questions, he had recommended the boat belonging to two brothers, professional fishermen named Peter and Andrew, who lived in Capernaum and whose boat was now anchored by the shore.

"Peter'll get you there," he assured me with a toothless sort of leer which I supposed he used in lieu of a smile, "and he's got a man with him what'll set you thinkin'!"

"Who is that?" I asked him, but evidently he had contributed his allotment of friendly intercourse for the day, and went back to the far more interesting occupation of counting his coins.

There was only one boat in sight which looked commodious enough to carry a number of passengers and strong enough to weather a storm. It had a yard of unusual length made of two spars spliced together and placed with its center against the mast. The sail, which was fitted to the yard, was square and portrayed some ingenius planning by experienced sailors. It was strengthened by ropes sewed across it vertically and horizontally, form-ing squares which, if rent by the wind, would be confined to that space alone.

Only one man was in sight, and I made my way across the tangle of fishing tackle and the nets which were drying in the late sunshine, to where he sat gazing thoughtfully toward the hills. I had to speak to him twice before he heard me.

"Are you the owner?" I called.

He got up and started walking toward me. He was beginning to be slightly bald, and his high forehead, his piercing black eyes, and his rather frail build gave him more the look of a man of letters than a fisherman.

"This is the boat of Peter and his brother Andrew, fishermen of Capernaum," he told me. "My name is Philip, and I help them with their business."

"I am Tribune Claudius Lysias," I said, "and I wish to inquire about the probability of engaging passage to Capernaum. Would you be able . . . ?"

A look of incredulity and delight passed over his face.

"Tribune Claudius Lysias! Sit down, sir, sit down! Wait! Let me make a stool clean for you to sit upon! Let me gather these dirty nets together and put them on the boat. You are not accus-tomed to the strong odor of fish!"

I searched my mind for the reason why a Jew, obviously of the provincial class in spite of his scholarly appearance, would extend such a cordial greeting. Usually persons of his type regarded all Gentiles with disdain and all Roman soldiers with suspicion and hatred. I watched him carefully as he piled the nets on the boat and walked back to where I sat. It occurred to me that perhaps I should remain standing so that I might be prepared for a sud-den attack in case the man's mind might be deranged and his attitude of friendliness change to as inexplicable an attitude of belligerence.

He seemed calm, however, as he drew a stool near to my own and sat down. "I must apologize, Tribune," he said, with a gentle smile, "I have heard your name called so often in the last few days that I had come to think of you as a close and treasured friend. I have a cousin whose name is Hannah who lives in Jerusalem, and it was her young son Caleb whom you rescued from the turbulent waters of the Jordan River where John the Baptist was preaching. Hannah tells the story to everyone she meets, and Caleb asks to hear it over and over. It has come to replace all the Scripture stories he used to beg to hear."

"I am sure you would have done the same thing, Philip, if you had seen a Gentile child in the water."

"You are a good man, sir," Philip insisted. "I cannot think how excited Hannah and Caleb will be if I tell them you are in Capernaum and that I have sailed with you across the lake. Which reminds me, sir, about the passage. I am sure you will be welcome on the boat, but I cannot say when we will be leaving. Our trips on this water used to be determined by the catch. We came and went as the fish were running, but now our lives are changed. Strange things have happened to the men who run this boat. I think of it many times. I think of John and his brother James who were once so wild that people called them the sons of thunder, and of how their father, old Zebedee, used to wring his hands and pray whenever their names were mentioned. I think of Peter, once called Simon, but I think most of myself. All of us are changed, but none of us, I think, so much as I."

"What changed you, Philip?" I asked.

"A man named Jesus."

I leaned forward on my stool. "Tell me about it," I said eagerly.

"It is a very long story, sir," said Philip. "I fear you would grow tired."

"Have you ever been in the inn in the town?" I asked him. "If you have, you can picture what a dull evening I have ahead of me. Unless you have work to do, I should like to sit here with you for awhile."

Philip walked to the boat, gathered up some nets which needed mending, came back and sat cross-legged on the ground, working on them. He began to talk. It was a long story. There was a moment when I stopped to ask about a huge bird at the edge of the water gulping a whole fish in its bill. He told me that it was a cormorant and that I would see many on the shore of the Sea of Galilee but that I would never see one which was not eating.

"Hannah's little boy says they are just like him," he told me, "that they are never unhungry."

Philip's story was so interesting that after many hours had passed in which I had held long conversations with several other people, I still remembered it vividly, and when I was in my room in the inn, before I would close my eyes for the night, I wrote it down as nearly word for word as I could recall it.

I record it here—Philip's story.

"Bethsaida was my home town, Tribune," he began, "as it was the home town of Peter and Andrew, although we all live now in Capernaum. They were both a little older than I, and I doubt if either of them would have known my name if someone had asked them suddenly.

"To me, Peter was a knight in shining armor. He was so daring, so confident, so able to make people laugh when he had broken the most rigid rules or had committed some offense for which I should have been soundly thrashed. Andrew was quieter and far more serious, but as far as I was concerned, he walked in the reflected glory of his brother.

"I was timid. Sometimes I have thought that it is as hard to bear as a physical infirmity. In my classes in the synagogue I had no difficulty in reciting something I had memorized, but when I endeavored to say the simplest words of my own, my tongue was like a stone in my mouth. At night I thought of clever replies and witty answers I would give, but when morning came all the cleverness and the wit were gone.

"'Just you wait!' my mother would say. 'Being slow as a boy will only help you to talk faster when you are a man. Things will be better!'

"It was not true. Things were not better, but worse. A timid, fearful little boy might be appealing, but a timid, fearful man was a thing from which people turned away in pity or disdain.

"It was April when I made the journey to Jerusalem—when I, Philip the timid, became Philip the man. It came about like this. John the Baptist was attracting widespread attention preaching in the wilderness of Judea. Andrew and his friend John of Capernaum had gone to the city and were attending all the meetings.

Peter, who had scoffed at Andrew for going, suddenly decided to make a gay pilgrimage of it, to gather a group together, go to Jerusalem, and see what it was all about.

"I hung around Peter. I hoped he might ask me to go too, but he never seemed to notice me at all. Finally my mother made a great pretense of wanting to go to Jerusalem. She asked several of our relatives to pack baskets of food and to plan to spend several days in the city listening to the new preacher, doing the spring shopping, and perhaps attending parts of the Passover Feast. My mother insisted that she could not go without me. She said she must have my help in pitching the tents, building the fires, and taking care of the camp. I knew what she was doing. I had seen her do such things many times, and though I loved her for it, my heart was sick inside.

"As we sat around the camp fire at night, it was worse than having stayed at home. I, Philip the timid one, sat with the old people. I could hear Peter and the others as they passed by. It was always Peter's voice which could be heard above the other voices, telling the tales he loved to tell, singing gay songs which would have made my mother blush if she could have heard the words. There was only one man in our group in whom I had the slightest interest—a man named Nathanael, not many years older than I. He had a flair for unexpected quips which made me listen to him and envy him.

"After we had been in Jerusalem for two days, I wished we would go home. We had been to the banks of the Jordan to hear the preacher, but his warnings, his fierce denunciations of everybody, left me more eager to get away from him than to go down into the water and be baptized.

"One afternoon, as the older people took their naps, I walked down into the city. Soon I saw Andrew and John and the preacher, John the Baptist, talking together. I wanted to join them, and after I had sauntered by several times, I summoned the courage to stop. Andrew spoke to me. 'Why, Philip!' he said, and all my timidity descended in full force. I could not answer, but suddenly they lost all interest in me.

"Coming down the street toward us was a tall young man. His head was lifted high, and he walked as if every step was a joyful adventure. His clothes were no better than the ones I myself was wearing, but he wore them as if they were the vestments of a king.

" 'There he is!' said John the Baptist. 'The lamb of God!'

"I did not know what he meant, nor did I greatly care, but I, Philip the timid, cared about the stranger! I felt somehow that he could understand me and help me. John and Andrew seemed to feel the same way, because without a word to John the Baptist they began to follow him down the street. I heard him ask them, 'What do you seek?' and they answered, 'Rabbi, where are you staying?'

"They went with him. With all my heart I wanted to tell him what it was that I was seeking. With all my heart I wanted to go with him. I could not.

"For a long time I stood looking toward where I had seen John and Andrew disappear as they followed the strange young man. The sun went down, and the lamps began to be lighted, but I could not leave. 'He may come back,' I kept whispering to myself, 'he may come back!'

"Several hours must have passed before I saw Andrew and John coming toward me in the dim light. Their faces were glowing with excitement. It was as if they were in possession of some strange new knowledge which they could not wait to tell. But they did not tell me—Philip, the timid one. They did not glance in my direction as they hurried by. 'Peter!' I heard Andrew saying, 'I must find Peter!' I could have told him where Peter was. I had seen him pass as I stood waiting, followed as he always was, by a crowd of laughing, singing friends.

"I went back to the camp outside the city gates. Lying awake on my pallet, I began the dreaming which I always did, dreaming which never came to fruition. Tomorrow, I told myself, I would go to Andrew and ask him where the stranger lived. Tomorrow I would go to the man himself and tell him all the things which made my life so dull and without purpose. I would tell him how every unexplained laugh, every quick glance between friends, every lift of the eyebrows, made me sure that I was the subject of ridicule. But even as I dreamed, I was not able to persuade myself that tomorrow would be different from today.

"Before dawn, while the others were asleep, I arose quietly, dressed, and started walking aimlessly toward Jerusalem. As I entered the Sheep Gate, I saw a man who seemed to be walking as I was, without a definite destination in mind. As the light became clearer, I saw that it was Peter.

"'Let me see now,' he said as he joined step with me, 'you live near us in Bethsaida, you went to the same classes in the synagogue down by the river, and you were smarter than we were, but you will have to tell me your name.'

"It makes me ashamed to remember how I muttered and stumbled as I answered, but Peter did not seem to notice. 'Why are you up so early?' he asked, but he did not wait for an answer. He had a rambling way of talking which was sometimes hard to follow, but it demanded nothing of the listener.

"'I tell you, I would not be up so early,' he continued, 'except that Andrew and John met a man named Jesus yesterday afternoon, and they kept me awake most of the night quoting Scripture and telling me all the things he had said to them. They are excited. They think he is the Messiah. Someone has told them that he sometimes goes to a garden called Gethsemane on the Mount of Olives at the rising of the sun, and they left the camp an hour ago, making me promise that I would follow. Anybody who can get my stolid brother Andrew excited ought to be worth getting up to see, so I must hurry!'

"I—poor Philip—wanted to go with Peter. As he walked away, all the hurt and frustration of my boyhood and my young manhood, all the disappointment and insecurity of my inept, unimportant, stumbling life seemed gathered together in my heart. I told myself it was no use, that I never would meet the man who had, for a passing moment, given me the hope that I might somehow come to be like other men.

"But I waited. I could not leave. I waited for a long time, as I had waited for Andrew and John. When finally I saw Peter coming, he was running, and there was the same look of excitement on his face which had been on theirs. But Peter stopped! He saw me, and he stopped.

"'A wonderful thing has happened, Philip,' he said. 'It was not at all as I had thought. I had expected to meet this man Jesus, have a dull talk with him about behaving better, being more like my fine and noble brother Andrew, and that would be the end of it. I had pictured him as a queer-looking rabble-rouser in strange garb like that worn by John the Baptist. I have seen many of them as they go about the country trying to change people like me. The moment I looked at this man, I wanted to be like him. This was a man's man. I knew he would not lecture me, and yet I knew he had all the things I only pretend to have. I knew he did not have to talk louder and sing more lustily than the others. He knew me. I felt that he had known me for a long, long time. He said to me, "You are Simon the son of John? You shall be called Peter." Something is ahead of me, Philip! I do not know what, but something is ahead of me!'

"Peter walked a little way, and then he turned back to call to me excitedly that he and Andrew and John were going with Jesus to Capernaum, that they were going to stop on the way in the village of Cana where they had all been invited to a wedding. I wished I had been asked to go with them.

"I started walking back toward the camp. I was so wrapped up in my own bitterness and self-pity that I was not conscious of the Passover crowds which passed by. Suddenly I felt a hand on my shoulder. It was Jesus, walking beside me.

" 'Follow me,' he said quietly, and was lost in the multitude.

"There had been a time when I—Philip the timid—would have thought he had asked me to do an impossible thing. I would have thought that since he had not told me where to meet him, or when, I could not possibly do as he had commanded. But it did not occur to me that I could not find him. Jesus had asked me to go with him, and that was enough. For the first time in my life I was master of a situation!

"It was wonderful! As I walked, I realized that even my walking was different. My head was lifted high, and my shoulders were back so that the air I was breathing seemed like elixir in my starved and contracted lungs. My mother's face, when she looked at me, was beautiful to see. I knew full well that as soon as she saw me she would realize the long-deferred answer to her prayers.

"I told them all I was going to Galilee, that I did not know whether I would return to Jerusalem or stay in my home. I had made a decision for myself, and I was about to carry it out. I was like a man, long imprisoned, who had suddenly been set free!

"As I started off, my bundle over my shoulder, I found myself whistling one of the gay songs which I had heard Peter singing so often in Bethsaida. I stopped once or twice and stretched my arms full-spread to the sky!

"Without warning, I had the feeling I had seen depicted on the faces of Andrew and John and Peter. I must tell somebody about Jesus! I must take someone to him! Nathanael!

"If I had been the old Philip I would have told myself I could not spare the time, that Jesus and the others would leave without me. But I was not the old Philip. I went back to the camp. I spoke to Nathanael without hesitation or stumbling, without fear of ridicule or rebuff. I spoke as one man speaks to another. Even when he smiled and asked, 'Can anything good come out of Nazareth?' I was not taken aback.

"I said to him, 'Come, and see!' "

+   +   +

The town of Gadara is situated about five miles from the Sea of Galilee with the Yarmuk River between, and as it had grown quite dark by the time I left Philip, I wondered, as I urged my horse along the unfamiliar streets, if the toothless old innkeeper would have extinguished the lights and locked the doors without concern about whether I got to my room or not.

I was relieved to see that the lamps were burning and that in the small room where old Eben had his desk he still sat counting his coins, and that two elderly women were sitting on a dingy couch near the door. As I passed, one of them reached out her hand and touched me on the arm.

"Sir," she said, rising and making a quaint curtsy, "I am mother-in-law to Peter, and I wish to say a word of thanks to you. It may seem strange to people from other countries that news can travel so quickly here, but in Capernaum where I live we have known for months about your saving the little boy. His mother, Hannah of Jerusalem, is almost like a daughter to me. You did a fine thing. You have changed the opinion of many of my people about the Roman soldiers. Old Eben tells me that you have been out to the seashore. I wish to ask if you have seen the boys. I worry about them."

"I have seen only Philip," I told her.

"I am much concerned when they are late," she said, sitting down again upon the couch. "There are many whispered rumors that now in every crowd where Jesus is, the rulers gather—watching him. They seek something of which they may accuse him and take him before the court. Peter is impulsive, and if anyone were to attack Jesus, he would draw that silly sword he insists upon carrying, and probably would get himself taken to prison or even killed. My daughter loves him dearly. If you have a mother, my son, you know how mothers worry!"

"I do indeed," I told her.

I was charmed by the sweet and engaging manner of this little old lady, and I walked over to the innkeeper's desk, picked up the only stool in sight, and placed it in front of the couch.

"My name is Elizabeth, sir," she said, "and this is my friend Joanna, wife of Herod's steward, Chuza."

Until that moment I had not paid particular attention to the other woman who sat on the couch, but as I acknowledged the introduction I was impressed by the sadness of her face and the dejected attitude which was evident, not only in her expression, but in the slump of her shoulders and the constant nervous movement of her hands.

"Joanna lives here in this inn," Elizabeth told me, "and I come over to see her whenever Peter's business brings him to the country of the Gerasenes. Joanna and I have been friends since we were girls together in Nazareth."

Joanna looked at me briefly, and I could see that there was fear and distrust in her eyes. She stood up, wringing her hands together. She made a quick, awkward little bow, mumbled something which might have been "sir," and left the room.

"Do not be surprised, my son, or disturbed," Elizabeth explained, patting the couch for me to sit beside her. "Joanna has grown strange and apart in the last few years. I feel sure I would have been the same way if I had led her kind of life. Occasionally when I am here she will talk and laugh as we used to do out in the hills around our home, but, more often than not, she is moody and preoccupied even with me. She is terrified of the Roman soldiers. I have told her about your brave deed, but she will not accept it. She says it is only some kind of trick to win our confidence. Of course, the things she has suffered have made her bitter and distrustful."

"She has had much sorrow?" I asked.

"Many people to whom you might put the question would answer that she has had none at all, but I could not agree. There are different kinds of sorrow, my son. Sickness and death are not the only things which can make the heart to lie like stone. Long waiting by a window as one plies the loom, lying alone through the dark nights, hoping until one knows there is no hope—these are things which can wither and decay like a cankerous growth in one's vitals."

"I am sure this must be true, Elizabeth. You make me eager to know what it is that happened to Joanna."

"It was so long ago. It was when Joanna and I were little more than brides. I had been married about a year, and Joanna and the handsome young Chuza only a few months. Our little houses were next door to each other, and we shared all our adventures and our mistakes. Sometimes it was I who went crying to Joanna because the cakes I had tried to make for breakfast had stuck fast to the sides of the heated pots in which I had tried to cook them. Sometimes she came running to show me a wild gourd which she had gathered thinking it was a cucumber, and when she touched it to her lips, had been burned as if with a live coal. Those were happy days, my boy, filled with excitement and with love. I shall never forget the morning when Joanna knocked on my door, almost beside herself with joy because Chuza had been chosen to go to Tiberias and become chief steward to Tetrarch Herod. Neither shall I forget the day she came back! She looked as if she had been turned into an old woman."

"Her husband had been killed?" I asked.

"Not killed, my son. A Roman soldier had met them at the gate to Herod's estate with instructions. Only Chuza was to remain, he said, any relatives were to depart at once for Gadara across the lake where suitable quarters would be arranged in the inn. Weekend visits at the end of each month would be allowed. The thing which broke Joanna's heart was that Chuza did not wish to give up his fine position. He tried to persuade Joanna that it would work out, that with his high place of responsibility and his large salary they could be happy. Joanna knew it was not true. She knew that Chuza's love for wealth and position were greater than his love for her."

"Does she ever see Chuza?"

"Only a few days each month. Now they are more like polite strangers than like husband and wife. When Chuza comes here, he is so full of his own importance that I cannot bear to stay in the room where he is. He never seems to notice the gloom of this inn or his wife's depression. He brings her great sums of money, and he thinks she is content. I worry about Joanna. Peter and I are planning to bring Jesus to see her, perhaps tomorrow if there is time. I hope she will not walk away from Jesus."

"Jesus is here? I think she will not walk away."

"We cannot be sure, my boy," Elizabeth said, a little wistfully. "There are many who walk away. He wishes to help people, but there are those who think they do not need him. I almost missed his help myself."

"You?" I asked, looking at her shining face, seeing how vital and alert she seemed in spite of her years. "I cannot think what you ever could have needed from him."

"Fever! Do you know about the fever which burns the body until it is dry and parched? Have you heard about the weakness, and the sweats which pour from one's aching frame until one yearns to return to the dry, parched skin again? My son, on the first Sabbath that Jesus was in Capernaum, I lay in my daughter's house with such a fever. I needed help, my son. I needed help from anybody. I was so drained of strength that I would barely speak to my daughter when she came into my room to minister to me, and when Peter came in, I thought I could not bear his booming voice and his abundant vitality.

"I had never heard of Jesus. It was late on that Sabbath afternoon when he came. Peter had already made his visit for the day to inquire about my condition, but he came in again. I could see that he was trying hard to be quiet and that he was being more careful than usual about knocking things over.

"'Mother,' he said to me softly, 'I have a friend, and I want you to meet him.'

"'No,' I thought to myself. 'No! I cannot bear company!' It terrifies me now, Tribune, as I think of it. I almost refused to let Jesus come into my room. There was something different about Peter's voice however, so I gave a reluctant permission. Peter went outside the door, and came back followed by a quiet young man. His quietness seemed to give me strength and courage. I held out my hand to him. He took it, and held it in his own—my hot, claw-like hand. He did not say one word. He held my hand tightly for a moment, and then laid it gently on the bed beside me. He put his arm about Peter's shoulders, and together they left the room."

"Were you disappointed that he did not speak?" I asked.

"I was not disappointed. You may find it hard to believe, but when Peter and Jesus had gone, I arose from my bed, bathed in cool water, found fresh clothes for myself, and went out to where my daughter was preparing the evening meal. When she saw me, she sat down at the table and began to cry. 'I did not think he could do it!' she said."

As Elizabeth walked up the steep stairs with quick, sure steps like a girl, I thought about Lazarus, young, confused and rebellious—about Nicodemus, with all the things which men count great—about Philip, shy, introspective and insecure—about this dear little old lady who had been sick abed with a fever. I thought of how different they were in their personalities, their stations in life, their ages, and their individual needs, and of how each of them seemed to have found the answer to their need in a strange young man named Jesus.

I was about to get to the writing I had planned to do when the front door opened and a giant of a man literally burst into the room. He must have been more than six feet tall, and he seemed to crowd the small lobby with his huge frame. Even before he spoke, it crossed my mind that this man must be the one Elizabeth had felt was too full of vitality and strength to fit into a sickroom.

This, I thought, must certainly be Peter. Now I could understand both Elizabeth's reaction to his virility and Philip's boyhood adoration of him. This man was a leader. His picturesque build, his reddish hair and beard, his great strong hands, gave him the look of one of the gods of Olympus, ready to do battle or to lift a world and hoist it onto his strong broad shoulders.

"You are Tribune Claudius Lysias?" he asked in his booming voice and did not wait for an answer. "Philip has been telling me that you wish to go to Capernaum with us. We will not be leaving until tomorrow morning; we have just returned from the day's work here in Gadara, and we are about to have our midnight supper. Philip likes you. He thinks you are a hero!"

Peter threw back his head and laughed. "I wager you get tired of all the Jews crying on your shoulder about getting the boy out of the river, Tribune. I know if I had been there, I would have jumped in just as you did, and then wished I could shed my wet clothes and all the weepers at the same time!"

I joined in his laughter. "You are right," I agreed. "Being a hero is no easy job."

"You may like it better when you eat some of Andrew's fried fish. You must remember that except for your noble deed, we Jews would not be found eating with a Gentile. Jesus tries to tell us that he has other sheep beside the Hebrew people, but we do not actually believe him. We do not understand how God could love anyone else!"

As we rode the five miles together, I felt a sense of exhilaration. Now I was going to meet the person who had been the subject of so many talks I had had since I arrived in Palestine. Now, at last, I was going to talk to Jesus.

When we came near to the boat I was amazed to find that my heart was pounding. I remembered how I had felt that first afternoon in Jerusalem, the strange desire to ask him who he was, what purposes he held, and now I was about to meet this man who was so human that people of every class and condition wished to be with him, and yet so filled with some strange power that he could reach out a hand and heal a sick body or a troubled mind.

"Where is Jesus?" I asked bluntly when the introductions were ended.

A man named Thomas answered. "He is asleep on a cushion in the stern of the boat. Multitudes crowd so about him that he never can find time to sleep. We are all keyed up over a strange incident which occurred this afternoon. But not Jesus. Although the experience distressed him more than it did any of us, the anger we felt he did not feel at all. He felt only sorrow.

"Another strange thing happened yesterday afternoon as we were making the crossing from Capernaum. A great storm arose. The winds blew, and the waves were so high they began to fill the boat. Even though we are used to the turbulence of this lake, and most of us know these waters as we know the streets of our own town, we were afraid. All of us were afraid—even Peter.

"Jesus had not slept the night before, but we almost resented it that he slept now that we were in danger. We awakened him. We said, 'Teacher, do you not care if we perish?' "

Thomas hesitated for a moment, looking at me intently.

"He stood up in a boat, Tribune Lysias," he said. "He stood up in the boat, and he spoke to the troubled waters as one might speak to a rebellious child, and the waters became calm. There was sorrow, or perhaps disappointment, on his face as he looked at us. 'Why are you afraid?' he asked. 'Have you no faith?' "

"I wish he were awake," I said regretfully.

As we all sat cross-legged on the deck, Andrew brought us the most delicious fish I had ever eaten. There was the same difference in the flavor and appeal of this freshly caught fish and the kind which could be purchased in the markets in Athens, as there was in the fruits and vegetables which I had eaten freshly gathered from the garden and groves of Martha and Mary in Bethany. I was glad that old Eben had served such an unappetizing meal and that I could enjoy Andrew's midnight supper.

Soon the men began to refer again to the unusual experience

of the afternoon. I was glad when Philip said to Peter, "Do not forget, Peter, that Tribune Lysias and I are hearing only snatches of what happened. Why not begin at the beginning and tell us the whole story? It may help all of you to understand it more clearly, as you seem to have varied opinions about it."

I smiled to myself as Philip spoke to Peter with the assurance one feels in speaking to a close and dear friend, and not at all as he had pictured himself to me earlier. I noticed also that Peter listened when Philip talked, and immediately followed his suggestion.

"It was like this," Peter began, and as Philip had told me, he had a rambling way of talking which required attentive listening, "numbers of people over in Capernaum who came here to visit, my own mother-in-law for one, have been telling about the terrible man living out in the tombs, as mad as can be, they say. When the town magistrates came with chains to bind him, he broke the chains, and they ran for their lives. He always went back to the tombs, seeming to get some comfort in living in the city of the dead. He took sharp stones and cut himself terribly on the arms and legs and body, and then he would cry all night so that those who lived near could not sleep. Often the guards from the Roman fort were called, but their prison would not hold him.

"Yesterday Jesus had been teaching the people since early morning, but suddenly, late in the afternoon, he told us we were coming to Gadara. He wanted to talk to the mad man."

"Does your friend Jesus never grow tired?" I interrupted Peter to ask. I do not know what I wanted him to answer. Perhaps I was hoping he might offer proof that this man was not human after all. Perhaps I hoped that Peter might answer that Jesus had no human frailties, that he did not know hunger or fatigue or pain. Perhaps I only searched for something which my pagan mind could refute.

That was not the answer I received. "Tired!" Peter replied. "I have seen him so tired that I have wondered how he could take one step from where he stood! I have seen him so tired, as he is tonight, that he falls asleep before he can eat, although he has told me how hungry he is. We are all strong men, Tribune, used to hard work. Look at me! I am an ox for strength! I tell you, sir, we are all weaklings when we try to keep up with Jesus. It is as if he has to finish something in a hurry!"

"I apologize for having interrupted your story, Peter," I said. "I was much interested. Please continue."

Peter looked at me as if he wished to burst into laughter. He put his big hand over his mouth and coughed slightly, and I realized that to these men my speech must sound stuffy and affected.

"Go on!" I said brusquely. "We are losing time!"

Peter smiled, and continued. He had not missed my quick change of manner.

"When we docked at Gadara," he said, "Philip went into the town to get supplies, and by the time he was out of sight, we saw the mad man running toward us. I tell you he was a horrible sight! Blood was all over his face and body and arms and legs. Some of the ragged, brutal cuts were still bleeding. His long hair and beard were matted with blood and dirt, and he had no clothes on at all. We are not fearful men, but if Jesus had not been here with us, we would have taken off on a run. The mad man did not seem concerned with us. He ran straight to Jesus, and he began to shout in a loud, hoarse, terrifying voice, 'What have you to do with me, Jesus, Son of the Most High God? I adjure you by God, do not torment me.'"

"Why do you think he addressed Jesus this way?" I asked.

"I do not know, and I do not know how Jesus kept from flinching as the man began to sob. He fell down in front of Jesus, and his whole horrible, bloody, naked body was shaking. He threw his bloody dirty arms around Jesus' legs, but Jesus spoke to him with the same authority in his voice with which he spoke last night to the angry waves. He rebuked the spirit of madness in him, and then he asked with infinite tenderness, 'Son, what is your name?' I suppose the man had not remembered for years that he had a name; he gave a strange, confused answer, and then he began to cry. It was no longer the terrible, hoarse sobbing which had been shaking his frame, but a gentle sort of crying, like that of a long lost child returned to his father's arms.

"Jesus lifted him from the ground; he put his arms around

that vile, filthy, repulsive form, and he helped him into the boat. The mad man was no longer mad.

"We all stood looking at each other completely speechless, but it was not the miracle which amazed us. We had seen Jesus perform many miracles. It was that we could see that Jesus loved this man! To him the blood and the dirt and the nakedness were as nothing. This horrible person was to him someone infinitely dear, and if there had been the need, we knew that he would have carried him in his arms."

I looked about at the faces of these men. Not by the greatest stretch of the imagination could one say that they were sentimental or neurotic or easily moved. These were hard-working, practical, down-to-earth men, used to the seamy side of life, used to fighting, to harsh language, to knowing what they wanted and going after it, but there were tears in their eyes now, and their faces were as sweet and as understanding as a woman's might have been.

"Perhaps Tribune Lysias would give us an opinion about the swine," suggested the man named John. "We have argued about it ever since it happened and have come to no decision."

"A strange thing that!" Peter agreed. "Do you possess any knowledge concerning spirits which sometimes seem to possess people, Tribune?"

"Very little," I replied. "There is a school in Greek philosophy which holds that they are the spirits of men, not necessarily always evil, but possibly even the spirits of those who lived during the Golden Age when there was the flowering of civilization and art."

"Well, what happened here this afternoon," Peter declared, "is enough to make anybody wonder. While all the things I have been telling you were taking place, a big herd of swine was feeding near by. About two thousand of them, I would say. Of course you know, Tribune, that a large part of the population here is Jewish and have no business dealing in swine, and suddenly the whole lot of them went running down the steep embankment into the sea as if they had become possessed with evil spirits. The herdsmen could not stop them, and when they had run back into the town to tell the owners, the whole lot came running toward our boat demanding to see Jesus.

"Jesus heard them, and he came out from the boat. With him was the man who had been mad. The blood and the dirt were gone. His hair and beard were washed and shining. He sat down quietly, and looked at the screaming crowd with intelligence and with understanding in his eyes. He was clothed, and in his right mind. It meant nothing to the crowd. The thing they kept screaming about was that their pigs were lost in the sea.

" 'Go away!' they yelled at Jesus. 'Depart from our shores! Our pigs are gone! Our money is lost! Go away! Go away!'

"A few picked up small rocks from the shore, and began to throw them. Tribune Lysias, the look in Jesus' eyes is something we will never forget. It was as if his heart were breaking—not for himself, but for them."

John spoke softly. "Rejection!" he said. "It is the one thing which can bring that look into his eyes. It is a sort of beaten look, as if children he loved had rebelled against him. It makes me remember the Scripture my father Zebedee used to read to James and me. I think it was the prophet Isaiah who pictured God as saying, 'I was ready to be sought by those who did not ask for me; I was ready to be found by those who did not seek me. I said, "Here am I, here am I," to a nation that did not call on my name.'

"When the anger of the crowd had spent itself, and the men had gone back into the town, Jesus went into the boat and began to gather food and clothes and blankets to give to the man who had been mad. He heals men's souls, sir, but he does not forget their need for food and drink and warmth."

"Will Jesus leave Gadara?" I asked them.

"Certainly he will leave. He will not force himself upon a man or a city. He was here. He walked upon their shores. They saw his power, but they could not lift their eyes from their pigs or from their flattened purses. He will leave, as they have asked him to."

"And the man?"

"He did not want to go back. He said 'Jesus, take me with you.' But Jesus answered, 'Go home to your friends, and tell them how much the Lord has done for you, and how he has had mercy on you.' "

"Mercy!" John said, almost to himself. "With Jesus there is always mercy. If men ask him to leave, he sends a man who was lost, and now is found, to tell of his wondrous works. Jesus and his love for men is now about to be proclaimed in Decapolis. Perhaps the day will come when they will forget their pigs and begin to marvel."

Galilee

It was a simple day. There was in it nothing of action, certainly nothing of excitement, and yet no matter how long my life may be, whether it is filled with sun or with shadow, whether it is one of high dignity or of obscurity, I shall not forget the day I sailed across the Sea of Galilee with Jesus.

As I write this down, it sounds as if Jesus and I were alone on the boat, and as I think of it, I feel almost as if we were. Other men were there, and strangely enough, their personalities were not overshadowed but enhanced by Jesus' presence, yet to me, it will always be the day I sailed with Jesus.

Sometimes there are eminent personages in politics, dignitaries in religion or education, sometimes people of royal blood, about whom one hears and whom one wishes to meet, but the interest is largely curiosity.

Except for the time when I had watched him driving the traders in oxen and sheep and doves, and the money-changers, out of the Temple of Jerusalem, and the brief glimpse on the day I had lifted little Caleb from the surging of the Jordan River, I had not seen Jesus. Yet the desire which I had and continued to have to meet this man face to face, to sit down and talk to him, was different from anything I had felt before.

As I made myself ready to set sail from Gadara that early morning, I thought again of the things Jesus had said to Nicodemus—words which were profound and thought-provoking. I remembered the simple story he had told Lazarus, of a rebellious boy leaving his home and then returning to his father's waiting arms. I thought of Philip and his insecurity, and the strength in Jesus' simple command, "Follow me!" I thought of Elizabeth, old and sick and discouraged, and of how she had needed no words, only the touch of his gentle, strong hand. I wondered what he would say to me. I was not a Jew. I was not profound, nor frustrated, nor ill. Perhaps, I told myself, he would not be interested in me at all. Perhaps he would find no time to speak to me.

As soon as I stepped on the boat, I saw him. He stood facing the sun which was beginning to make a red glow behind the hills surrounding the Sea of Galilee. As I approached he came forward to meet me. "You are the young man who helped me in the Temple," he said. "I am glad you are going to sail with us."

The words could not have been more commonplace, but suddenly my heart began to sing. I was glad for the red glow of the sun. I was glad for the blue waters which were beginning to surround Peter's boat. I was glad Jesus had remembered, and for the words he had spoken.

When I try to recall other words which he spoke on that day, I cannot remember. I know that it was a day overflowing with contentment. There was good conversation. There was laughter. It was apparent immediately that the men adored him. And although he shared in all their tasks and did not set himself apart, he showed the same kingliness, the same dignity, which I had seen in the Temple when he stood with a harmless little whip in his hands.

Peter was there, of course, loud-talking and lovable, and Andrew his brother, quieter and more serious. Philip was there, no longer timid, but secure in his place of responsibility. Philip's friend Nathanael was there. The quick-tempered brothers John and James were aboard, sometimes dreamy, sometimes poetic. Thomas was there, a bit opinionated, a bit stubborn when he wanted to be. There was a man named Judas—dark, thin, with a sullen face and eyes which shifted a little when he talked. I learned that he was not a Galilean as the others were, but was from the south of Palestine. I learned also that he was the treasurer of the group, and carried the bag into which they all contributed their share of the necessary expenses.

I thought that if Judas had been under my command in the Roman army, I never would have trusted him with the money. Judas talked big. He had big ideas which the others did not

seem to understand. Several times I noticed him as he sur-
reptitiously counted the coins in the bag with the same look
in his eyes which I had seen in the eyes of old Eben at the inn.
Once I saw Jesus looking at him.

Suddenly and inexplicably, I wished for Mariamne, and
knew it was as incongruous a wish as a man could have.

A queer group indeed. Nine Jews and one Gentile. Eight uneducated men of the working class, and one man used to the
things of culture, study, and, gracious living. Eight men who
belonged to the people of a conquered land, and one officer in
the army which the people despised.

Yet, as we sailed that day, there was no difference between
us. There was no Jew, no Gentile, no rich, no poor, no bond, no
free. We were all as one in the presence of a young man who
somehow, without apparent effort, brought us all together in a
strong, sweet bond of fellowship.

Capernaum of Galilee was the center of an area of more than
two hundred teeming, thriving cities, towns, and villages, some
of them so close together that it was difficult to determine where
one ended and the other began. As the center of a manufacturing
district it was ideally located. The Sea of Galilee was on the
south, providing a route for the boats plying back and forth from
the cities of Decapolis on the southwest and from the provinces
of Ituraea, Trachonitis, and Gaulonitis on the northeast.

In addition to the sea traffic, Capernaum had the advantage
of being situated at the crossroads of three great inland highways,
the one from Tyre and Sidon, the one from Damascus, capital of
Syria, and the one which ran down to Jerusalem. It was often
said that if one wished to see masses of people, one need only
stand in Capernaum where these three great highways crossed.
When we disembarked from Peter's boat in the dusk of that
late afternoon, I knew the saying was literally true.

I noticed that there were impressive buildings in the city.
The most outstanding, and the one I noticed first, was the new
synagogue on the east side of the downtown section. It was built

of gleaming white stone, with four great Corinthian columns at the entrance. Its shining dome made a beautiful picture against the darkening sky. There was a fairly pretentious Roman fort, and some of the other buildings were larger and more ornate than I had expected.

Pilate's written instructions told me that the centurion in charge of the Capernaum fort was a man named Ananelus and that he would have been apprised of my arrival within the week. I found Ananelus to be an elderly soldier, who, though kind and hospitable, seemed uneasy and distraught. It was as we were having our evening meal that he began to confide in me the cause of his obvious preoccupation. He told me that ever since he had received the information that I was to arrive in Capernaum, he had been unable to eat or to sleep, because he felt certain I had been sent to relieve him of his command.

When I assured him my visit did not concern him in any way, he leaned back and began to eat.

"When a man is as old as I am, my son, to be removed from the only work he has ever known would not be easy to bear. I found myself thankful last night that my wife no longer lives. The disgrace would have broken her heart. Now, however, I really would like to tell you why I was troubled." He added, smiling for the first time, "It is possible your young mind has conjured up fantastic behavior on my part of which I never could have thought."

"You have made me curious," I told him, "but unless you wish, you need say nothing further."

The old enjoy reminiscences, and perceiving that Ananelus was eager for a listener, I leaned back on my cushioned bench, listening as I ate.

I asked no questions, at first because I did not wish to break his line of thought, and later because of my interest in what he said.

"It began a long time ago, when I was a young soldier like you. I had been sent here as the commanding officer in this post of the army of occupation. I hated Palestine, as I imagine you hated it. These Jewish people with their one God, their prayers, their rites and ceremonies, were of no more interest to me than the cattle and sheep which roamed the hills. I was as little interested in religion as any self-satisfied young Roman could be. Let them pray, I would think, no god will take a holiday to listen.

"Most of the people here are laborers, and although they had no money with which to erect a place of worship, they would go down by the river on their Sabbath day, and one could hear them chanting their mournful psalms for a long, long way. I am not sure just when I began to listen. There was something oddly soothing and comforting about it. At first it was only the strange music which interested me, and as I listened from the window of the fort, I would hum along with them as they sang. Later I began to go forth on those mornings when they met and sit on a rock somewhere near enough to hear but never near enough to be seen. Even though there was much which I could not understand, I listened intently. I knew that the words were words of homesickness and loneliness with a quality which soothed the heart of a boy in a strange land.

" 'By the waters of Babylon there we sat down and wept,' they sang, 'when we remembered Zion. On the willows there we hung up our lyres. For there our captors required of us songs, and our tormentors, mirth, saying, "Sing us one of the songs of Zion!" How shall we sing the LORD's song in a foreign land?' Homesickness. They knew about that.

"The more often I listened, the more I came to understand, and soon I was staying to hear, not only the singing, but the reading of their Scripture. Could it be that they knew a God who heard them when they prayed, I asked myself. From Jupiter, one stood afar off and shouted, hoping that he might hear. Could it be that they knew a God who cared? Of their God they read, 'As a father pities his children, so the LORD pities those who fear him. For he knows our frame, he remembers that we are dust.'

"I listened to their history. Never had I heard anything to equal it for drama and suspense and excitement. Their heroes were great strong men chosen by their God to represent him here on this earth, trusting them, teaching them, pleading with them to hold fast to the high place to which he had called them. And yet the people always seemed to fail. Conniving and consorting with pagan nations who had chariots and horses, forgetting that they were the ones who had their God. The conquerors of old were known to him by name, though they knew him not, nor cared that he was God. They read it from their Scriptures—he knew Sannacherib, king of Assyria; he knew Nebuchadnezzar, king of Babylon; he knew Cyrus, king of Persia. Under their little flashes of glory, he said that he would kindle a burning like the burning of a fire—and he did. He said he would go before them and break down iron gates and bronze doors—and he did. Through all history their God had stood in control of kings and nations as he carried forth his eternal, unchanging plan.

"It was not his power which won me, nor his might, but the fact that he was always with them. In poverty, in loneliness, in exile, he was there, never bent on punishment but on rescue. I could not get away from a God like that! He became my God, and I needed no other!"

Ananelus stopped to wipe away a tear. "You are wondering, Tribune, what all this could have to do with my apprehension concerning your arrival. It is this—I began to help these people. Only a little at first, because I know Roman officers are not encouraged to contribute large amounts to local enterprises for fear of establishing a precedent, but when they pooled their funds, hoping to save enough to start a small place of worship, I built them a synagogue! It is beautiful! You could not have missed seeing it as you came into town. It has everything a synagogue should have, and a good, devout man named Jairus is the head ruler. I tell you, if it were built of pure gold, I could not be more proud! On the first day we met there, we were like those who rebuilt the Temple in Jerusalem after their seventy years in captivity. The old people cried, the young people sang, and you could not tell the crying from the singing."

I was touched by the deep conviction and the courage of this old soldier. I assured him that if his action in building the synagogue ever was questioned, I should contend that nothing could lead more surely to an amicable relationship between the people of two countries than such understanding and cooperation. Seeing how much it had meant to him to have a listener, I began to ask him questions which had puzzled me for months.

"Centurion," I said, "tell me about the different political

parties in Palestine, the scribes and the Pharisees, for instance."

Ananelus laughed quietly. "I do not know why it is that they always have been spoken of together, since there is no bond between them, and since there are many scribes who are not Pharisees and many more Pharisees who are not scribes. The scribes are not a party or a religious sect at all. Their foremost duty is the copying and recopying of the Scriptures. Although parchment is made of the skins of sheep or goats and is durable, the skin has to be subjected to a strenuous process of drying and tanning in the hot sun before it is suitable for use, and when scrolls are handled as much as the Scriptures are, they wear out rapidly."

Ananelus explained that the work of the scribes had led to their becoming the interpreters of the law as well; that when a question arose concerning a local situation, if no precedent could be found in the Scriptures, the scribe himself handed down a decision, and that decision became a law. Until, he said, so many laws had been added and such a mass of tradition appended, that most people had no idea where God stopped and the scribes began.

The Pharisees were, he explained, a political party comparable to parties in other countries which championed the cause of the common people. Their oneness with the proletariat, however, was a political tenet only, for they often publicly praised God for their own superiority. As a religious sect of the Jewish religion, they were the ritualists, the over-pious, and they allowed their rites and sacrifices and tithing to take the place of their belief.

The Sadducees, he said, were of the aristocracy, caring nothing for the great unwashed and having many private matters of business as their chief concern. They were rationalistic, believing in nothing supernatural. "Sometimes I wonder," Ananelus added, "if they believe in God."

He became serious. "I may seem to speak lightly of these men, Tribune," he said, "but hold no misconception in your mind about their power. These men, usually opposing and hating each other, will work together if their easy, convenient religion is threatened, and they can manipulate the legal murder of any person who dares to oppose them."

Ananelus rose from the table, slowly, cautiously, as the old move. "I have enjoyed the evening, Tribune, but the hour grows late for an old man. I regret that my servant, Alexander, has not returned. He is my friend rather than my slave, although my father bought him at the slave market many years ago. He is near my own age, and he was given all the educational advantages which were accorded the youth in our family."

"Does he share your belief in the God of the Jews?"

"He does, Tribune, and you, a Gentile as we are, will not find it easy to comprehend when I tell you that both Alexander and I have gone farther. We have found, in a young man named Jesus, a carpenter from the small town of Nazareth, the fulfillment of all the Jewish prophecies which we have come to believe."

"You, Centurion! A Gentile, a pagan!"

"Do I detect a small note of wistfulness in your voice, my son? Is it possible that you have met this man?"

"I have met him, sir."

"Then sit down again. I must tell you something which happened to Alexander and me."

Again I listened without questions, without interruptions.

"It was an ordinary day," Ananelus began. "I have learned from much living that most important things come into our lives on an ordinary day. The sun was shining. Alexander was preparing breakfast as he does each day of our lives. It was none of the things it might have been—dark, or angry-looking, or foreboding. Just a day at nine in the morning when we always break our fast. Suddenly Alexander called out in terror, 'Master, come quickly! My legs will not move!'

"When I reached him, he lay face down on the floor. I have known little of illness, but somehow I remembered the small fruit called coriander which my wife had sometimes used as a carminative for the stomach, and although I do not know why I thought it might help his legs, I lifted his head a bit and tried to press the fruit between his lips.

"At that time neither of us knew Jesus, but we had heard rumors of startling cures he had effected in the countryside. Alexander began to mumble. At first I could not understand his words, but soon I was able to make them out. 'Get Jesus!' he was saying.

"People who live in a neighborhood like mine take little interest in the magic performed by itinerant preachers. I asked everyone I passed, and although some had heard his name, no one knew where I might find him. Someone suggested the house of a fisherman named Peter.

"When I reached that section of the city, everybody knew him. Their faces would light in love, sometimes in adoration, when I spoke his name. An old lady answered my knock at Peter's door, and her face too seemed aglow when I asked for Jesus. 'Out on yonder mountain, Centurion,' she said. 'Follow where the crowds are greatest, and you will find him.'

"I followed the crowds and when I came to the foot of the mountain, the multitude was so dense I could not push my way through. There was intense excitement. A leper, they said, had been touched by Jesus. The touch had healed him. They had seen it with their eyes.

"Then I saw Jesus. I pushed desperately through the throng. I cupped my hands about my mouth and shouted, 'Lord, my servant is lying paralyzed at home in terrible distress.'

"In spite of the insistent babbling of the multitude, he heard me, and he answered as quietly as if we had been in a room alone. 'I will come and heal him,' he said.

"Tribune Lysias, until that moment Jesus had been to me nothing more than one of the many preachers of Palestine who sometimes possessed a strange power to heal. Now, without warning, a great sense of unworthiness swept over me. It was as if I stood in the presence of royalty. 'Lord,' I said, 'I am not worthy to have you come under my roof!'"

"It was not the miracles which set him apart. There was a compelling gentleness about him, there was strength and courage for the taking, but there was authority also. Suddenly my mind recalled the words which Alexander and I had read together in the early morning from the prophet Isaiah, and I repeated them imperfectly to myself. 'The sun shall be no more your light by day, nor for brightness shall the moon give light to you by night, but the LORD shall be your everlasting light, and your God will be your glory.'

"Jesus turned to the multitude, and they hushed their babbling to hear what he would say. He put his hand on my shoulder. 'I have not found such faith in all Israel,' he said. They muttered. They did not like it. But their opinion did not concern me at all. I cared only for his promise, 'Go; be it done for you as you have believed.' When I came to my door, my servant was singing in the house.

"He was well?"

"He was well!"

Ananelus had started up the stairs when there was a knock at the door. "I will open it for you, sir," I called.

It was the woman who had brought me the pot of red soup in Jerusalem. She held a little boy by the hand. "I am Hannah," she said, "and this is my son Caleb. Ever since Philip told us you were in Capernaum, he will not let me rest for begging to see you."

"I am glad you came, Caleb," I told him.

He ran forward and threw his arms around my legs.

"I love you," he said. "I love you like anything!"

I arose early the next morning. As I dressed, I looked out of the window, and not far away I could see the Roman fort. I could see the soldiers marching up and down, their swords gleaming. I could hear the sharp orders crackling like flying arrows in the crisp morning air. They looked businesslike. No wonder, I thought to myself, the people hated them and were afraid. I looked at the sunshine gleaming on the dome of Ananelus' synagogue—a synagogue built for Jewish people by a Roman officer who had made their God his own—and I thought the gleaming of the dome was brighter than the gleaming of the swords.

I was excited. This was the day I would see Mariamne. I had inquired of Ananelus, but he knew nothing of Matthew except that he was a wealthy man who served as publican in this northern district. I realized that I must keep my mission secret and be careful to follow Pilate's orders, so I could not show an obvious interest in Matthew. It seemed that the best plan would be to take my notes, find a crowded place, and let things take whatever course they would.

My steps led me to a rather shabby section of the business district. The wayside merchants were setting up their dusty, shopworn wares, and the farmers were coming in from the outlying areas with their late crop of figs, a few still fresh, but most of them having been dried in the sun. There were carts filled with corn that also had been dried in the sun and then parched, and which people passing by on their way to the wharves would buy and hold in the palms of their hands, eating as they walked. I soon came to a small open-air eating place, and although it was hard for me to face the unappetizing array of food, I made some pretense of eating so that I might feel free to sit in this crowded place and orient myself before making definite plans for the day.

The few small tables filled very quickly, and I was relieved to see that it was a pleasant-looking, well-dressed man who took the vacant seat beside me. He was talkative and affable, and it did not take me long to discern that he was a man of education, far above the dirty, nondescript men who crowded each other at the surrounding tables. I wondered why such a man would be eating at this unattractive place.

As if he sensed my wonder, he said to me, "I do not make a practice of eating in this vicinity, but the ladies in my household are sleeping late this morning because of a party which we gave for a guest last evening, and the servants were in the midst of cleaning up the aftermath, so I slipped out quietly to transact some business with these merchants here. I suppose you know that there are more desirable eating places on the other side of Capernaum."

"I felt sure that would be true," I answered, "but like you, I had a reason for being here, and I thought that ordering a bit of food would give me the right to occupy one of these tables. I am Claudius Lysias, sir, tribune in the Roman army stationed in Jerusalem."

"Tribune Lysias!" he exclaimed. "I am Matthew, publican of this Capernaum district. I have heard your name many times in the last month both in connection with your fine deed in saving the small boy who fell into the Jordan River and from a guest of my daughter Susanna." His eyes were twinkling. "Susanna waits impatiently to meet you, but I must confess that I fail to detect the Apollo-like qualities which I have been led to expect. I have learned from experience, however, that young girls look out upon the world with dream-filled eyes."

I joined in his laughter. "If they did not, sir, some of us rather ordinary fellows would be in sore straits."

"Where are you staying?" Matthew continued cordially. "The inns in Capernaum are beyond bearing. My house is large, and I shall be glad to have you for whatever time your business keeps you here."

A dilemma indeed! I had come to this town for the sole purpose of investigating this man and his questionable activities as tax-collector. I wanted to be with Marianne, and this opportunity was beyond anything for which I could have hoped. My responsibilities as an investigator seemed to be dwindling with surprising speed. I arose and began crowding my notes into a small leather case.

"I spent last night with Centurion Ananelus, sir," I answered. "I must go there to collect my luggage and to thank him for his hospitality."

Matthew smiled at my eagerness. "Sit down," he said, "the girls will be sleeping for another hour. We can become acquainted as we wait. I am glad you have had the opportunity of spending some time with Centurion Ananelus. He is a man of surprising qualifications. Roman officers and Roman soldiers stationed in our city have always been hated and feared, but Ananelus has done more to wipe out hatred and fear than all the scripture reading which could have been done in all the synagogues here in Galilee."

"He told me last night how he had come to believe in the God of your people and also of how he and his servant had come to see in a young man named Jesus the fulfillment of all your prophecies."

"I too, Tribune," Matthew said earnestly, "I too, believe in Jesus."

"Matthew," I told him. "I am Greek with a background of philosophy. My family has not been one to spend much time in thinking of religion, and I have been amazed since my arrival in Palestine at how religion seems to permeate your land. On my first day in Jerusalem I saw Jesus for a moment or two in the

Temple, and yesterday I sailed with him across the lake from
Gadara. It has seemed that every conversation of length which I
have had has somehow included his name. I have never met a
man like Jesus."

"Nor have I. I do not speak easily of these things, but I am
preparing now to give up my position as tax-collector and to follow him wherever he goes. I am planning to offer my money and
my house to be used as he desires. I intend to dedicate myself to
him and to his purposes."

"What are his purposes, sir? I had supposed he made no plans
but let each day take care of itself."

"I am a hard business man, Tribune, and for a time it distressed
me to see the apparently aimless way in which he carried on his
ministry—calling a handful of unknown, uneducated men to follow
him, going from place to place with no seeming plan of action
other than the need of some common beggar or some demented,
useless man. But if you could have stood with me on the mountainside and could have heard him as he carefully enunciated his
purposes for the kingdom he has come to establish, you never
again would say that anything he does is without insight and
discernment."

"A kingdom, sir!"

"A kingdom, Tribune. I have always been a student of the
political affairs of the Gentile nations and of their history. As I
listened to Jesus, I knew I was hearing the carefully considered
manifesto of a king. It did not deal with platforms or with consti-
tutions. It had nothing to do with the money a man possesses, the
lands he owns, or the clothes he wears. It had to do with the man
himself. It was concerned only with what a man is."

"Would that be a practicable basis upon which to establish a
kingdom—to have a low regard for money and for material possession?"

"You misunderstand me. Not once did Jesus discount the value
of these things. He only made it plain that they are not the essen-
tial issues in life and never should be given precedence over those
things which are."

"Will he find followers who can accept such a theory?"

"Not many. There were those there that day who were disappointed. Many had hoped he had come to establish a Jewish world empire, one which would be greater in political and military prestige than that ruled by David and Solomon. There were some who had expected to hear him stir the people by talking about hating the Romans and about the need to demonstrate that hatred by fighting. Many who listened turned away when Jesus talked about loving one's enemies and doing good to those who oppress us. They came down the mountainside shaking their heads and muttering that they were mistaken in him, that he must be beside himself, and that when the first glow of excitement was over, Jesus would be forgotten."

"I see you have not forgotten him, sir. I should like to hear what it was in his speech which seems to have made such a change in your ambitions."

The man beside me at the table sat quite still for a moment. Then he replied, thoughtfully. "I think if I were called upon to choose one precept out of all he said that day, it would be a short sentence which has stuck in my mind like a burr. It has caused me to re-evaluate my whole standard of behavior. It is this. 'Whatever you wish that men would do to you, do so to them.'"

"But sir," I remonstrated, "while those are excellent words and all might do well to follow them, surely you cannot think that they are original with Jesus. Is it not true that your own Hebrew master, Hillel, once said, 'Do not to your neighbor that which is hateful to yourself,' and that our Greek philosopher Socrates taught five centuries ago, 'Whatever stirs anger when done by others, that do not to others'?"

"You are correct, Tribune, up to a point. The teaching of Jesus, however, is vastly different from the teaching of those scholars of long ago. The teaching of Jesus involves action. He teaches that we do something. Those great men whom you mention teach that we are not to rob or to kill. Jesus teaches that we must pour oil into the wounds of a man whom others have robbed and left for dead, that we must take him to an inn and furnish money so that the innkeeper can take care of the wounded man until he is well again."

"It is not going to be easy to be a follower of Jesus," I said. "I still do not understand why you feel it is necessary to give up your wealth. Do you think Jesus demands this?"

"I think he lets each man make his own decision, my boy. I have made mine. When I first began to believe in him, I thought as you do that I could keep my wealth and continue in my business, but while a half-way mark may be the goal of some followers and for some it may be sufficient, it cannot satisfy the need which is in my heart to serve him with all I have. I have come to this neighborhood today to return to some of these people money which I have taken from them just for the privilege of renting these vile quarters. You have said it is not easy. It is not. Do you think I do not find it difficult to impoverish myself by returning money to people whom I hold in the lowest regard?"

I could not miss the enthusiasm and the submerged excitement which possessed this man as he talked. He was not tall. He was round about his middle, and his chins had multiplied and dropped a bit. No one could possibly have mistaken him for a young man, and yet there was in him the ebullience which one associates with carefree youth.

I could see that Matthew, the publican, needed no investigation, because he no longer existed.

When we reached the rather exclusive section of Capernaum where Matthew's house was located, I saw at once that he had amassed great wealth and that he liked rare and beautiful things around him. His home was as pretentious as the town-house of Nicodemus in Jerusalem and in the same excellent taste. It had its own private beach and a formal court which might have been planned by one of the eminent designers of gardens in Athens. I wondered if this man realized what he was giving up. I wondered if he had any conception of the life he would lead if he went with Jesus. I remembered the men who had sat barefooted on the deck of Peter's boat, eating with evident enjoyment, but without benefit of silver or napkins. I wondered if Jesus would want Matthew to be a follower, if the other men would resent having him join them.

A servant met us at the door with the information that Susanna
and Mariamne had eaten breakfast and had gone straight to the
house of Peter where it was reported that Jesus was teaching the
people. I had no time to indulge in the sense of disappointment
which overwhelmed me at not seeing Mariamne. Matthew's face
was glowing. "We must hurry!" he said excitedly. "We must not
miss a word!"

The distance to Peter's house was not great, but the change in
the surroundings was sudden and almost unbelievable. The type
of houses changed. The sea was not far away, but it looked like
a different body of water. There were no clean white sands leading down to inviting blue waters on the shore near Peter's door.
There were fish nets everywhere, and rows of all kinds of merchandise piled together without system or care. Peter's court was
a mass of tangled juniper shrubs with a few white blossoms
holding on stubbornly in the autumn winds.

There were the usual fig trees, and an ancient olive tree with
a broken limb was hanging almost across the front door. I thought
as I drew nearer, however, that any growing thing would have
had small chance of survival in the mass of people who were
crowded around Peter's house. It was all we could do to maintain
our footing in the multitude who jostled us and each other. Elbows
were thrust into ribs, and each person seemed bent upon reaching Peter's door before the other.

I had been in tremendous crowds many times, but I had never
seen one to compare with this. I had been hurried and pushed, and
had done my share of it when attending the gladiatorial contests
in Rome. I had endeavored to make my way to an advantageous
spot to hear some prominent speaker in the agora in Athens. I
had joined with the thousands who went to watch the people in
their rites and ceremonies in the Parthenon as they did obeisance
to the goddess Athena, but those crowds had been made up of
excited, gay, healthy people. I had never seen intensity to compare with the intensity of this multitude.

Here there were men hobbling along on crutches or canes,
falling down and being stepped on, picking themselves up and
starting again. Here there were women with babies in their arms,
babies who were making pitiful, whining little noises so that one

knew they were sick and weak. There were children everywhere. Some were holding on to their mothers' skirts, some losing their hold, becoming fearful that they were lost and giving vent to sounds which were far from weak or pitiful.

Along the sides of the road, being stepped on and fallen on, were the long, sad, heart-breaking rows of the desperately ill. The blind were here, fumbling along with a cane, and then with only an outstretched hand to guide them as the cane became lost and trampled under the hurrying feet. Here were the dumb, making garbled, guttural noises as they pushed along with the rest.

I was overwhelmed with sadness and pity as I saw them and heard their clamorous shouting. "I was first! I was first!" some shouted. "He must heal my baby! He is so little and so sick!" Others were saying, "It will not last! His power will run out! Let me through! I must get to him quickly!"

I felt ashamed that my uniform made the people fall away, and let us pass into the room where Jesus was speaking. I wanted to take the sick babies from their mothers' arms and place them in the arms of Jesus. I wanted with all my heart to help the blind, or to lift an emaciated form from the pallet on the ground, but I did not dare. I tried to remind myself of the caustic remarks of Tribune Julius concerning my need for soldierly toughness, but it did no good.

Coming into the room where Jesus was speaking was like reaching a quiet port in the midst of a storm. Inside there was not a sound except the sound of his voice. Many who had hoped to be healed had pushed their way into the room, but their frenzy, their impatience, their feverish haste, had disappeared. They listened now to his every word as if his words had been the object of their coming.

The man who spoke so quietly at one end of Peter's room was a teacher of incomparable ability. I had a deep admiration for my own father and his ability to make clear and understandable any subject which he presented, but his listeners all were scholarly men, eager to grasp the subject at hand. This was a strange crowd, made up of provincials with meager education, and men from Jerusalem and Damascus whose learning would be of the highest type, and yet, as I looked about, I saw the same intense interest, the same comprehension of the things Jesus was saying, in the faces of one as in the faces of the other. There was profound teaching here, but there was also marvelous, astonishing simplicity.

"Come to me," Jesus was saying. "Come—all of you! Come if you are weary and heavy-laden. Come if you are sick or blind or dumb. Come, and I will give you rest."

And a sense of rest was filling the room, like incense burning in a temple.

There was illness and blindness and lameness and minds burdened with troubles and fears, but in the presence of Jesus these things seemed to fade and grow dim, and there was momentary surcease from worry, and respite from pain.

I had become separated from Matthew in the crush of the crowd, and was glad I had been pushed against the only window on the side of the room where I stood. As I lifted my face to the cool air from the outside, I caught sight of a strange, small procession going up the narrow, steep stairs which many people in Palestine build on the outside of their houses. These stairs are made to reach the roof, which is usually of tiles and earth and can be removed when there is need to lower a large object into the room below. A roof of this type was often used also for drying figs and dates and root vegetables in the autumn and winter, and for an open-air sleeping room in the summer.

At first I could see only one man. He was going up almost backwards, and he seemed to be holding some sort of cloth or blanket grasped tightly in his hands. Soon I saw that there was another man on the step below him in almost the same position, and with the same material held tightly in his own hands. As they passed upward and out of my view, I could see plainly what it was they were carrying. It was a man! It was a man lying on a thin mattress. On those steep stairs, it was almost as if he were standing on his head, as they evidently had not thought of facing him in the other direction. His face was toward me, and when I saw the agony there, I knew it mattered nothing to him whether his head was up or down. I had never seen such torture pictured on a person's face, and I hope I may not again. When the other two men, who were carrying the lower end of the mattress, had passed up the stairs, I was glad to have the agonizing picture out of my view. It crossed my mind that they might be taking him to the roof, hoping the warm sunshine would benefit the horrible ailment from which he was suffering.

When I turned my attention back to the room, I noticed that just in front of me two fat and successful looking Jews had moved into an advantageous position to see what was taking place. The wide phylacteries and the enlarged borders of their garments marked them as men probably from Jerusalem, and probably Pharisees of high standing. They were whispering in loud, sibilant whispers. "Make a note of this crowd," one was saying. "The publican Matthew is here. The whole crowd is made up of publicans and sinners."

Leaning against the wall, gazing intently at these prosperous men with a calculating look in his eyes, was the man Judas.

Far over on the opposite side of the room Philip was standing. By his side was his cousin Hannah and little Caleb. Caleb caught sight of me almost at the instant when I saw him, and he raised his hand and shouted "Trib. . . . !" but his mother put her hand across his mouth. The smile she sent me across the crowd was warm and beautiful.

I could not understand the hatred I saw in the faces of the men in front of me. I thought surely they could not be feeling such an emotion toward Jesus. At this moment he was standing with a little girl of two or three in his arms and she kept patting his cheek with her tiny hand as he talked. I remembered what Elizabeth had told me in the inn in Gadara about the fear she felt when her son-in-law, Peter, was away too long. She told about the envy and hatred which the important religious element in Jerusalem felt, and how those who loved Jesus were afraid it might become a real threat to his life and to the lives of those who followed him.

Suddenly I had no more time for contemplation. There was great commotion in the room. Dust was falling on our heads and shoulders, and pieces of broken tile were dropping everywhere. Women screamed, men made a rush for the door, and little children began to cry, but almost immediately Jesus quieted them. I do not remember whether he spoke or not, I remember only that he held one hand high above his head, and in a moment it was as quiet in the room as when we entered.

Then I saw what was happening. Those four men, who had so laboriously carried the sick, suffering man up those narrow stairs were now letting him down at Jesus' feet. I had to turn my eyes away. He was less a man than he was a writhing mass of pain. His feet were swollen and twisted out of shape. His hands were almost grotesque in their red and torturous helplessness. His neck seemed rigid, and his mouth was wide open as he gasped for breath in the choking dust. I felt that I must push my way out of that room. I myself was physically ill, but it was only for a moment.

Jesus leaned over and took one of those twisted hands in his own, and he spoke to the man quietly. "Son," he said, "do not be discouraged. Your sins are forgiven."

Immediately the man changed. His mouth closed, and he breathed naturally and with ease. His poor, misshapen hands and legs relaxed, and he lay inert upon his pallet. There was such tense waiting and expectancy in that room that one could almost reach out and touch it. The men just in front of me looked at each other with an evil sort of triumph in their eyes. That triumph, however, could not compare with their expression of surprise and dismay when Jesus addressed his next words to them. They had not spoken one word concerning the sick man, not even a whisper, because I was so near I could not have missed hearing them. But now Jesus was looking directly into their faces.

"Why do you think evil in your hearts?" he asked them. "Would it be easier to say to this man, 'Your sins are forgiven,' or to say to him, 'Get up and walk'?"

Their faces were not only fat, but they were scarlet in their confusion. One of them began picking an imaginary thread from the other's shoulder and dropping it with elaborate carefulness onto the floor. The other had sudden and urgent business with his finger nails, and began to examine them with scientific intensity. Jesus did not take his eyes from them, however, and now the entire company was turning from the sick man who lay so quietly, to look at these strangers in their fine robes and with phylacteries bound on their foreheads and on their arms.

I thought that they would never forgive him for this.

Jesus was unperturbed. "But that you may know," he continued, "that the Son of man has authority on earth to forgive sins...."

And now he turned to the man who only a few moments ago had been a frenzied, writhing lump of flesh, and he said, almost without expression in his voice, "Get up, my son, take up your pallet and go home."

I, Claudius Lysias, Gentile and pagan, wanted to rationalize what I was seeing. I wanted to discount the fact that there was nothing here which would permit me to say that a superior will had overwhelmed a weaker one, that there was nothing here of magnetism or transference of strength from one body or one mind to another. I could not. I knew that the command had been as simple as a father might give to a son about a simple and unimportant matter.

I saw the man who had been drawn, twisted, and helpless getting up. I saw him lean over and pick up his pallet. He even took the time to fold it neatly and to put it across his shoulders. It was as if he moved in a dream. He put one foot in front of the other, tentatively at first, hesitating for a moment as if afraid, and then looking back at Jesus. It was all he needed. Suddenly he seemed to realize what had happened, and he began to shout.

"Praise God! Praise God! Look, everybody! Look at my feet! I can walk! Look at my hands! I can work again! I must find Mary. She works in the market place, but she need work no longer. I can earn bread. I can buy food for her and for the baby! Praise God!"

I could not blame him that in his excitement he forgot the four who had sweated and strained up those narrow stairs with their heavy burden. But Jesus did not forget. The crowd was breaking up now, and the men had pushed their way into the room. I saw Jesus go to them, put his hand on one shoulder and then the other; I could not hear clearly what he said, but I thought I made out the words, "When I saw your faith."

Matthew joined me as we went out the door. When we reached Peter's courtyard and the street beyond, we saw that the sick, the blind, the lame, and the dumb were still there, but their faces were lighted now with a great thanksgiving. They reached out trembling hands to the healed man as he passed by. They spoke words of congratulation, encouragement, and joy. There was in them now none of the selfish eagerness to push each other aside— to be the first. We heard them saying to each other, "We have seen strange things today."

We heard them glorifying God.

+   +   +

Neither Matthew nor I had caught so much as a glimpse of Mariamne or his daughter Susanna in the crowd. Matthew asked as we walked away from Peter's house if I would go with him to his office to gather together some records he needed in order to determine the exact amounts of money he had been overtaxing his fellow-citizens.

"Tribune," he said to me as we walked along, "a most disturbing thought came to me as I watched Jesus today. Perhaps he cannot use a man who has done the things I have done. I know that the men who are his followers are no angels, but they have not lived in open graft and injustice as I have done for so long. They are not hated in Capernaum—in all of Galilee—for being a vassal of the Roman government as I am. Perhaps Jesus may feel that instead of being the help I want to be, I might become a liability to him and to his cause."

I did not say to Matthew that almost the same thoughts had been in my mind. I, too, wondered if Jesus would want Matthew.

We came to the tax-collector's office down by the gate, the Seat of Customs where the boats come in from across the Sea of Galilee, and went inside. As Matthew gathered together his papers, suddenly we heard the same sounds we had heard earlier in the day when we had come near to Peter's house. Jesus and the crowds.

I went to the door and looked out, and far down Matthew's street I could see them coming.

I turned back to speak to Matthew and was amazed at the change in him. His hands were shaking. He was pushing the scattered piles of tax records together as if he wished to hide them, but could not.

"Lysias," he said, "I know what has happened. They have told him. Those crowds would not be walking on my street without a cause. When they have reason to transact business here they stand outside the door, because this office is owned by the Roman government. It is Gentile property. Even then, they turn aside and spit upon the ground. I have seen them many times. It is the Jewish gesture of hatred and contempt."

I had heard of the gesture from Tribune Julius in Jerusalem, and I wondered for a moment if it could be possible that Jesus—leading them all—would stop outside Matthew's door and spit upon the ground.

I went outside the office and stood in the morning sunshine. I did not know why. It was almost as if I meant to protect Matthew. But I could see them plainly now, and I remembered Philip's words, "He walks as if every step is a joyous adventure."

When they reached the door, Jesus paused—the disciples and the crowd waiting, as if for a clue.

Jesus went inside, walking on Roman property as if it were part of the world he owned and loved.

He spoke only two words, "Follow me!"

Matthew's plain, middle-aged, businessman's face was like the face one might imagine on the messenger of the gods. As Jesus left, Matthew began to fill a great leather case with the tax records. He tucked under his arm a crude-looking article which seemed to have been constructed by an amateur worker in carpentry.

It was a square of parchment fastened to a roughly hewn board. Matthew dusted it off carefully and set it up against the closed front door of the customs office. I could see the words on it.

"Office of Tax-collector Available to Reliable Man. Apply to Pontius Pilate in Jerusalem," it read. On a separate line was written, "Only Strictly Honest Man Need Apply."

"You were not going to miss a chance, were you?" I asked.

"I was not!" Matthew said positively.

Suddenly he started running down the road after Jesus. He turned back and called to me, "Wait! I will be back in a moment!"

When he returned, I thought I had never seen a man so excited or so happy.

"Listen!" he said. "I have asked Jesus and his men to come to my house for the noon-day meal. We must hurry! I am sure the servants can add something to last night's concoctions. We must invite everybody! We will go and get the girls. They will be at home now. You and Mariamne can take one part of town and Susanna the other. We will invite all my helpers in the tax-collecting business. We will invite the lame, the blind, and the dumb. We will invite the ones who are sick, and if they cannot come, tell them that another meal will be arranged soon, and I will send horses to bring them. Invite everybody!"

"Are you sure you will have room for so many?" I asked.

"I have a mansion which I have built with the money of these people. I should think that I owe them a meal."

Matthew threw back his head and laughed. It was the laughter of a man who suddenly has found something for which he has searched all his life.

When I entered Matthew's house, Mariamne was standing in the center of the great entrance hall waiting for me. "The servants told me you were here," she said.

I held out both my hands, and she came toward me with her own outstretched, and I took them in mine.

It was a good day.

Not long before noon Susanna started out in the district of Capernaum with which Mariamne was not familiar. Mariamne and I went from house to house in the section where Matthew lived and where there were many summer cottages such as the one owned by Nicodemus and his family.

The response to our invitation to attend Matthew's noon-day feast was not always completely cordial. Some seemed sincere in their reasons for declining, saying they had previous engagements, but there were many who were cool and aloof. When I remembered, however, that these were the wealthy Jews, I could well imagine that Matthew's heavy taxing of their extensive properties, and then building a house which outshone them all, might not have made him popular as a neighbor. After many refusals I began to fear that Matthew was going to be disappointed, and I did not want to see him lose any of that contagious joy which had been so evident as he planned this meal for Jesus.

But the sunshine was as warm as if it had been spring instead of autumn, and the breeze from the lake was soft and balmy, and I was walking with Mariamne. I did not worry too much or too long.

When we returned to the house, I could see at once that I need not have been troubled at all. The beautiful formal garden was no longer formal or very beautiful. The court, which had in it a sparkling fountain surrounded by exotic flowers and a small but exquisite marble statue, was beginning to look more like a market place than a court. The expensively furnished reception room which was across the back of the court, was also changing character by the minute. Dilapidated coats and cloaks were hanging across the backs of the luxurious couches, and I saw that one had been flung carelessly over an intricately carved ivory lamp stand. It had a jauntily rakish look.

Mariamne and I made our way through the throng to the next room where a huge banquet table was laid in readiness for the coming feast. I thought to myself that, however reluctant some of the high and mighty had been to accept Matthew's invitation, the poor had not been so particular. Perhaps they had felt as Matthew himself had suggested, that he owed them a meal, and I supposed also that many had seized upon this opportunity to see the inside of a house of such elegance.

Standing in this room, in the choicest and least crowded spot, was a group of men I had not expected to see. Two of the men had stood in front of me at Peter's house that morning. Three more had been added to their number. They had seemed to feel such hatred for Jesus, even before he exposed their critical thoughts, that I supposed they would not join any crowd which gathered about him. Yet here they were, smiling and obsequious, as if they had been the favored guests. I made my way to Susanna and whispered in her ear, "What about those men? Did you invite them?"

"No," she said. "I am sure no one invited them, but it is a custom in our country for people who have not been asked to a party to enter the house as long as there is room, and to stand along each side of the table at which the invited guests are seated. There is nothing to be done about it, although I was surprised, after what happened at Peter's, that they would want to come."

"Gathering evidence!" I whispered back.

When Matthew had seated Jesus in the place of honor, he clapped his hands, and the servants began to serve the meal. I was seated near the far end of the table with Philip on one side of me, and Thomas, John, and his brother James on the other. I had not seen these men except for a passing glance since the day we had spent on the boat, and I was eager to talk to them again. I was not so pleased when I saw the carping, conniving Pharisees standing directly behind us. Immediately they began to address the disciples.

"Why," the speaker for the group asked with a sneer, "does your master eat with tax collectors and sinners?"

There was a momentary silence, and I saw that the men were not prepared to answer. I hoped that the Pharisees might have the courtesy to let their question end any further effort to join the conversation, but I was soon able to see that I had not begun to understand these men. I had not begun to realize that their endeavor to break the surge of popularity, the intense love which the people had for Jesus, was something they would not relinquish easily.

"Why is it?" another in the group insisted. "Tell us, you men who believe he is the Son of God! If he were, he would never associate with these people. If he were, he would be in Jerusalem. He would be where the righteous people are. He would seek out the chief priests and the elders, the important leaders and those of us who know the law and keep it to the letter. Tell us, if you can, why it is that this man, in whom you have put your trust for eternal life, would come here to this house, the house of a despised publican, and would sit down with these people."

The room was quiet now. There was consternation on the faces of those who only a few moments ago had been talking and laughing. One could see that these poor, unimportant guests at Matthew's party realized how much they had to fear from the

Pharisees standing at the end of the table and speaking so sternly to the disciples.

I wished that I had known more of the history and the prophecies of the Jewish people, so that I could have answered for Philip and the others whose education and opportunities had not equipped them to compete in a verbal battle with these captious Pharisees. But I had no need to answer. From the other end of the table Jesus answered. He stood up, and his voice came with the same kind of inner strength which I had heard on my first day in Jerusalem when he had plaited small ropes together and had driven from the Temple those who were profaning the house of God. He spoke with dignity, and he spoke with authority.

"Those who are well," he said, "have no need of a physician, only those who are sick. Go!" he said to them sternly, "go and learn what God meant when he said, 'I desire mercy and not sacrifice!'"

I—a Greek, a Gentile—could see the picture he was painting of these important Jews as plainly as if he had drawn it on Matthew's wall. One could see that these men who delighted in the sacrifices of bulls and goats had no mercy in their hearts for their fellow men! John had spoken of it back there on the boat when the people had asked Jesus to leave their shores. "Mercy!" he had said. "With him there is always mercy! He never gives men up no matter how they have despised and rejected him."

I knew that this was true. I knew somehow that Jesus did not have in his heart the feeling of hatred toward those Pharisees which filled my own. Deep inside, something told me that his great, gentle, tender arms were wide open even toward them. They did not want his love or his forgiveness. They thought they did not need it.

A shocked stillness filled the house as the people realized that Jesus had dared to put to rout those influential and powerful men. They were afraid, for themselves and for him. I was afraid for him too. I knew that those religious leaders who were now leaving Matthew's house, had lost their coign of vantage for the present moment only.

Suddenly, in the stillness which followed, there came the sound of a man's voice. At first it seemed as if it was coming from the street, and then from the court, and then from the reception room. Gradually it came closer, until it was just outside the room where we sat. "Help me!" a man was saying, "help me get to Jesus!"

I saw him standing in the doorway. There was such agonizing despair on his face that I supposed him to be in the throes of some terrible pain. Directly behind him, almost supporting him with their arms, were Ananelus and his servant Alexander. Seeing the robes which the man wore, I decided he might be the head ruler of the synagogue—Jairus—of whom Ananelus had spoken. The stark tragedy in his face lessened slightly when he caught sight of Jesus, who at the moment he heard the importunate voice, rose from the table and started toward him. The man thrust himself forward from the arms of those who held him. He ran forward, and fell sobbing at Jesus' feet.

"My little girl! My little girl!" he sobbed incoherently. "We did not think she was so sick! We thought it was only a cold! Now she burns with fever and is convulsed with chills! Her throat is closed! She cannot breathe! The doctor has left, he says he can do no more. He says she is as good as dead. Please come to my house! Please come and lay your hands on her so that she may be well again!"

People began to cry. A little ashamed, I brushed a tear from my own cheek.

I wondered what Jesus would do. He was the guest of honor in the house of this wealthy man who, only a few hours ago, had begun to follow him. Jesus surely would not dare to offend Matthew. This great house could be of inestimable value in helping the sick and the homeless. Matthew's money would buy food for those who were starving, it would buy clothes which were warm and comfortable in the bitter cold of the Galilean winters. I wondered how he would choose, since the meal had only just begun.

There was conflict and indecision in my mind, but it was obvious that there was none in the mind of Jesus. When he reached Jairus, he stooped over and lifted him to his feet, and immediately, without a word, started walking with him toward his house. I looked to see what effect this would have on Matthew, who had gone to such effort and expense to have this feast prepared.

Matthew was putting on his hat. Susanna had thrown her shawl over her head, and she and her father led them all, the rich, the poor, all that throng, with their food uneaten. They seemed to have no other thought than to go where Jesus was going.

As we walked along, people came out of the houses we passed. They joined us, and sometimes paused for a moment to shout back to those who were in the rear of the houses or the stores so that they, too, could follow with the crowd. The multitude became so great that I found myself lifting my head as high as I could to get away from the actual sensation of suffocation.

I never would have believed that anyone could have changed positions in that throng, or that there was the vaguest possibility of moving from one place to another, but soon I felt someone tugging at my hand. Glancing down as well as I could while resisting the force of the crowd, I could see that a person, so tiny that at first I thought it was a child, was squeezing her way slowly from the back of the crowd to the front. When she raised her face to mine, I saw that it was a woman who was neither old nor young. There were deep lines in her forehead, and the lines from her nose to her mouth were almost like furrows. There were dark circles about her eyes which looked as if they had been painted there. Although she was so tiny, and looked so weak, there was a kind of fierce determination in her lined face, and an almost deathlike grip in her hands as she raised herself to a standing position by my side.

"You are going to get hurt!" I said to her. "The best plan is to stay in one place and let the crowd push you along."

"I cannot!" she said positively. "I must get through! I may not have another chance! I must get to Jesus."

"Then I will help you," I told her, and almost gasped in surprise at my own answer. I did not know the woman. I did not know why I had said that I would help her. There were undoubtedly many in that crowd who wanted to get to Jesus, and I could not help them all. But she had taken me at my word, and had tucked her thin, little arm in mine. She lifted her face to me in complete confidence.

"I will not need to speak to him," she said. "If you can get me near enough so that I may touch the hem of his garment, that is all I ask."

"You must have a pressing need indeed to brave this crowd when you are so tiny."

"It was my only chance. One does not choose."

"Are you ill?"

"For twelve years I have known nothing but illness. I am a Jewess, my son, and our laws, although they are right and good, are sometimes very cruel. I am not allowed to enter the Temple or a synagogue. Because of the affliction from which I suffer, I have been excommunicated. I am not allowed to stay in my own home with my husband and my family. It is the law. For twelve years I have worked, whenever I was able, and with whatever money my husband has been able to get to me, I have gone from one doctor to another, but instead of becoming better, I grow worse as I grow older. If we can only get near enough, Jesus will heal me."

"We will get you near enough."

Uniforms are most advantageous when it comes to exerting a bit of influence. I did not often set out to use mine for that purpose, but for some reason the cause of this tiny woman had become my cause, and I could not bear to see her unswerving faith in Jesus disappointed. I began to use my most executive manner and to speak in my most authoritative voice. "Step aside, please," I would say, "step aside, and let us pass through."

Finally we came to the front of the procession where Jairus and Ananelus and Alexander were leading the way to Jairus' house with Jesus a step or two behind. The four of them seemed to form a kind of small island, and I was surprised that a crowd of this description should have possessed the innate delicacy to let this man who was in such deep distress stay with his close friends and with Jesus, without coming too near.

And now the woman needed no more help. She was where she wanted to be. She stooped over and picked up the hem of Jesus' robe, and pressed it to her lips. Immediately Jesus stood perfectly still. "Who touched me?" he asked, quietly.

Those around looked at him in amazement. "Who touched you? How could we know in all the press of the crowd who follows?"

And then Jesus saw the woman. She no longer touched his robe.

There were many other women near, and yet he looked at her. She was trembling now and afraid; all the fine courage and determination drained from her tired little face, and when she saw Jesus looking at her, she fell down at his feet. Her words poured out like a torrent. She told him everything, how long she had been sick, how her husband had been forced to divorce her and to take her children from her, how she was not allowed to enter a place of worship, her desperate need only to touch his garment. I could not tell what she expected, whether she expected anger, reproof, or further separation from the people, but there were none of those things in Jesus' voice when he spoke.

"Daughter," he said, "your faith has made you well. Go in peace!"

As he leaned over and lifted her from her knees, I saw the ecstasy in her face. I saw also the face of Jairus. It was filled with dark agony. The time consumed in healing the woman had been only a moment or two, but it was as if he could not bear to have Jesus delayed for one single precious minute which might mean life or death for his little daughter. From down the street, I saw three men approaching. They came straight to Jairus, and I could tell by their clothing that they were probably servants in his household. I pushed forward a step or two. I felt I must hear what they were saying.

"Sir," they said gently, "your daughter is dead. Why trouble the Teacher any further?"

Jesus put his hand on Jairus' shoulder. "Do not fear," he said. "Only believe! Your child will be well again!"

Jairus believed him. The crowd believed him. I believed him. I knew it was not possible. I recounted the alarming symptoms of which Jairus had spoken, how the physician already had left the house before Jairus came for Jesus. I remembered that the servants had just come from the child's bedside, and I had seen the sorrow in their faces. I remembered that they had stated plainly, "Your daughter is dead."

Yet I believed what Jesus said.

Be careful, Tribune Claudius Lysias, down-to-earth Roman soldier, Gentile, pagan, brought up in the philosophy of Epicurus which long ago abandoned the search for truth, seeking nothing more in life than true pleasure by experience. Do not go overboard about this strange young man. He will have to fail sooner or later. He healed the sick man this morning, but this child is dead! All the evidence points to it. You are building up to a terrible disappointment. Go easy! Get hold of yourself!

These were the words with which I tried to draw my mind into its usual channels. They were the stern words with which I endeavored to compel myself to think thoughts of scepticism and doubt concerning things which one could not see or hear or touch, only feel. It was no use. I believed what Jesus said.

When we reached Jairus' house, the yard was full of people. They were wailing and weeping and beating their breasts. "Ah, a pity!" they said. "She was so pretty! She was so good! She was so sweet! She was their only child!"

Jesus spoke very quietly, but somehow in the tumult, people seemed to hear him and to listen. "Why do you make a tumult and weep?" he asked them, "the child is not dead but sleeping."

In their amazement their tears ceased, and they stopped their wailing and the beating of their breasts, but not because they believed him. They did not. They had been inside that house, and they knew death when they saw it. They laughed him to scorn.

Jesus motioned to Peter and to John and his brother James, and he put one arm about the shoulders of Jairus and one about the young woman who had run out to meet them, and he went with them into the house.

The waiting was almost unbearable, and when I saw big, strong Peter come out of the house wiping his eyes, my heart sank. Death had been too much for Jesus. I felt sure he must have failed. I walked over to Peter, and for some reason which I could not understand, I began to whisper. I suppose I felt that if Jesus had not been able to help the child, I did not want to bring disillusionment to those who believed, or to give satisfaction to those who doubted him.

"Too bad!" I said.

"Too wonderful, Tribune!"

"Too wonderful? What happened? Tell me, Peter."

"She was lying on her bed, sir, and she did look like an angel; she was so white, and her golden hair was spread like a halo across

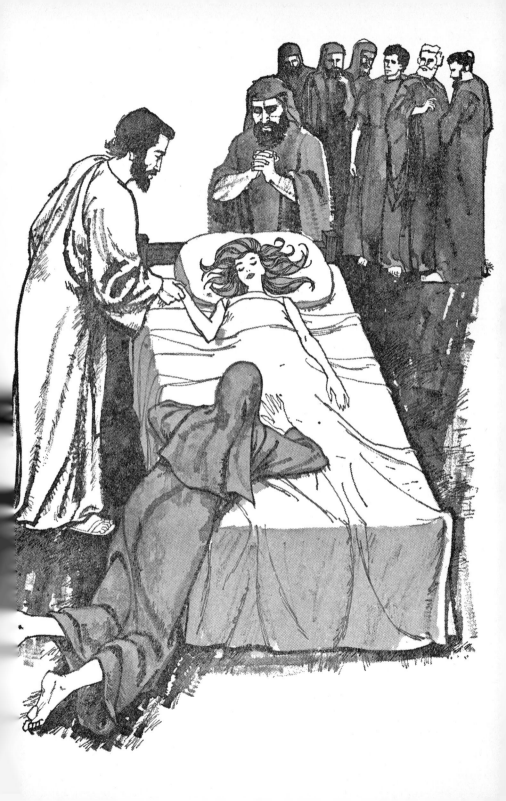

her pillow. Jesus just stood there looking at her for a minute, and then he took her tiny, cold hand in his own, and he spoke so softly we could scarcely hear him. He said, 'Get up, little girl!' And she did! I expected that he might say some profound words about eternal life, or about the power of death, or even something which we would not be able to understand. Do you know what he said, sir?"

"What did he say, Peter?"

"He turned to her mother and he said, 'Get her something to eat.'"

When Jesus and James and John came out of the house, the people were strangely quiet. They had heard what Peter said, but they seemed unable to grasp his meaning. Then, through the door came a little girl. She had a piece of bread in one hand and a small cake in the other.

The people began to laugh and to cry and to shout! She was well. Jesus had not failed. Death had not been too much for him.

The week which followed that incredible day in Capernaum was a week of unalloyed joy. My conscience troubled me occasionally when I took time to wonder if Pilate would have approved had he seen me relaxing so pleasantly in the home of Matthew when he had planned with such care to keep secret the real reason for my circuitous journey through Palestine. I argued with myself that since Matthew was no longer a publican but an open follower of Jesus, and since Capernaum was the last stop on my journey, there was no more reason for secrecy. Sometimes I would formulate in my mind the convincing explanation which I would include in my report.

I had temporarily forgotten Pilate's careful attention to details and his network of investigators. He had told me—at the time he was giving me the assignment of looking into the unethical behavior of the tax-collectors—that he had common soldiers stationed all over the country whose duty it was to report the integrity and the behavior of any man whom he wished to place in a strategic position. It should not have surprised me when in the week following Matthew's drastic change in character and position, in no more than the length of time it took a message from Pilate to reach Capernaum, I received a note from him saying he was pleased to hear of the change in Matthew and to know that I had been invited to stay in his home.

It was a blow to my feeling of high importance as a private investigator for the Roman procurator of Palestine to find that my own actions had been constantly watched and reported. I tried to tell myself that this was Roman thoroughness and efficiency, that this was the way they had become conquerors of the nations that had not felt such eternal vigilance to be a necessary or a dignified procedure.

After a small period of deflation in finding that I was not only investigating for Pilate, but being investigated by him, I began to be glad that Pilate was cognizant of all the details of my stay in Capernaum, and soon I could smile to myself and wonder who was watching the soldier who was watching me. I was continuing to discover also that the procurator, while highly efficient and untiring in building his own prestige in Rome and in Palestine, possessed a surprising store of understanding and kindness. His message to me was couched in the most formal language, commending my work and the secrecy which I had been able to maintain by making voluminous notes concerning the people, products, manufacturing facilities, and other matters of that nature. At the end of his message, he discarded all formality and wrote, "You have done a good job. Take a week of vacation in Capernaum. I hear you are not completely dissatisfied with your host or with his other guest from Jerusalem."

Matthew had not wavered for one moment in his determination to dedicate all that he was, and all that he possessed, to Jesus and to his cause. He was making plans to leave immediately with Jesus and the other men on a journey through the many cities, towns, and villages surrounding Capernaum. The great house was still there on the seashore, surprisingly clean and polished after the onslaught of the crowd that had attended Matthew's feast for Jesus; the servants were there to care for it, and Matthew was sincerely cordial in his invitation to me to remain as his guest for as long as I could stay. Remembering, however, that he was

leaving, I had demurred, thinking that even in the informal so-
ciety of Capernaum of Galilee, it might seem odd for a young
tribune to be visiting in a home where there was no chaperone
and where there were two attractive girls. Matthew saw my hesitation, and patted my shoulder reassuringly.

"You are right, Tribune," he said, "I can see you do not wish
to correct your host, who is so much older, on a matter of social
procedure, but I have not been careless about the wagging tongues
of the populace. I have invited a life-long friend, who was a
girlhood friend of my wife's, to come for a visit. She lives near
here in a small inland village, and she is always glad of an opportunity to come to Capernaum and enjoy the sea breeze and
the relaxation of having servants to wait on her. She has never
married, and her life is not easy. By the way, she is the twin
sister of Thomas, the follower of Jesus, whom you have met. We
have never known Thomas except very casually, but Thomasina
is like a member of the family. You will like her, Tribune, even
though sometimes she seems to bristle rather easily, and you
need have no fear, you young people will be chaperoned to the
last possible demand of propriety."

Aunt Thomasina was a large woman with an abrupt manner
which, one felt at once, might cover an inner softness of heart.
I began on the first day I met her to address her as the girls did,
and, although she did not refer to it, she seemed pleased. Although, as Matthew had said, she chaperoned with unrelenting
vigilance, she did not seem to disapprove of the long talks which
Mariamne and I had after we had finished our daily swim in the
warm waters of the lake as we sat on the beautiful private beach
which was back of Matthew's house.

I was happy with Mariamne. I could not define the happiness,
nor did I try to any great extent. She was not an exciting girl
like so many of the girls with whom I had fancied myself in love
during my school days. She was not beautiful except for the brief
moments when something in the conversation stirred her heart.
I could think of many things which she was not, but one thing
I knew, I was happy when I was with her.

Susanna was a delightful hostess in her father's absence. I had
liked her as soon as I met her, and her bubbling gayety made

her rather grotesque limp sink completely into the background. On her right foot she wore a great clumsy shoe which, Mariamne told me, was made for her by a special shoemaker in Jerusalem. It looked odd in comparison with the small and dainty sandal on her other foot, but she never seemed conscious of it and never hesitated to do anything which other girls of her age were able to do.

One morning when Mariamne had gone into the town to do some shopping, Susanna and I had a swim together, and I saw that she swam quite as well and as easily as I. As we sat on the beach in the sunshine, I could not resist asking her a few questions. She seemed so far from being sensitive about her affliction that I felt certain she would not object to my real interest in her.

"You swim so well, Susanna," I said, "I have been wondering if you can dance also."

"Indeed I can," she answered, gayly. "My foot looks heavy and clumsy to other people, but I have had it since the day I was born, and I suppose it seems as natural to me as the other. I have a wonderful father, Claudius; he never let me feel for one moment that I was different from other girls or that I needed pampering or extra consideration. I was never treated here at home, either by my father or by the servants, in any way which would call the slightest attention to my affliction, or which would engender any sort of self-pity."

"Do you never wish to be rid of it?"

"Of course I wish it! Any normal girl who loves good times, and likes to have the boys interested in her, would wish to be like other girls, but I have not let it make me the least unhappy or make my friends uncomfortable."

"Susanna, I cannot keep from asking you this. Do you believe as your father does about Jesus, and if you do, why do you not ask him to heal you?"

Susanna smiled her gay, contagious smile and then she asked, "Claudius, can you keep a secret?"

"Secrets are my forte!" I told her.

"Well then," she continued, "long before my father began to be interested in Jesus, there was a group of women and girls here in Capernaum who met every week to study the history and prophecies of our people. We had to meet more or less secretly because in Palestine women are not thought to be equal in understanding with men, and although we knew that Jairus, the ruler in our synagogue, would not be too hard on us if he found out, we realized that if our study came to the attention of the chief priests and elders in the Temple in Jerusalem, we might find ourselves in grievous straits, in spite of what Jairus could do to try to help us. This study group was organized by a delightful old lady who lives here in Capernaum with her daughter. Her name is Elizabeth, and she is the mother-in-law of Peter who follows Jesus."

"I know Elizabeth!"

"You know her? Then no matter how or when you met, I am sure you know also how Jesus healed her. She never meets anyone for the length of time it takes her to relate it without telling about her miracle, and I am sure no one can blame her for it.

"It was soon after she was made well again that she invited a small group to her daughter's house, and after she had served us her specialty in small cakes, she asked if we would like to come there every week and spend some time in searching the Scriptures. Fortunately she had access to the history and the prophecies of our people because, for a long time, she had been helping the scribes in rolling the scrolls as they were recopied. Since Jesus had moved to Capernaum, all of us had been seeing things we had never expected to see, and we were very interested in the idea of trying to learn more from the Scriptures than the women and girls were taught in the synagogues."

"You said, 'since Jesus moved to Capernaum,' Susanna—has he not lived here for a long time?"

"His home is in Nazareth, Claudius. It is a queer little town off the main highways and about twenty miles from here. I do not know why, but people always speak of it in contempt. When Jesus began his public ministry, however, he went first to Nazareth. He taught there in their synagogue, but the people would not believe him. They followed him out to one of the three bare scarps on the edge of town, and they tried to push him off. One of the boys who lives in Nazareth rides over here to see me quite often, and he has told me that he was there that day. He says he heard them as they planned to be rid of Jesus. He says he saw Jesus pass through that crowd of rough, fanatical men as if they had been harmless little boys. He says they had no power in his presence."

"I wonder what the people of Nazareth think now."

"My friend told me the last time he was here that they all come flocking to Capernaum, or to any of the towns on this side of the lake where Jesus is speaking, and that they hang on his every word. They look on as he heals the sick, the blind, the lame, and they shake their heads and say to each other sadly, 'He could do no mighty works in Nazareth because of unbelief!' I think they are right, Claudius. I believe sincerely that the only thing in the whole world which can limit his power is the unbelief of the people themselves."

"Susanna, I must ask you again, but if you do not wish to answer, please do not hesitate to tell me. Why do you not ask Jesus to make your foot normal like the other?"

"I have asked him, Claudius."

"You have asked him! He has refused in spite of your faith in him? I can hardly believe it!"

"Perhaps you will understand why when I tell you how it happened. It was on a morning after our meeting at Elizabeth's. My heart was full to overflowing with the certainty which was now in all our hearts that Jesus does indeed fulfill the Jewish prophecies. We had read the very words which told of his birth in Bethlehem in the book of the prophet Micah. We had read in Hosea that he would be called out of Egypt. We had seen that many of the prophets said he would be called a Nazarene. I had no doubt. I left the others, and I sought him out. Claudius, before I had time to say one word, he spoke to me. He called me by my name, and he said that he was glad I had come. He said that he needed my help!"

"Susanna," I interrupted, eagerly, "on the day when I sailed on Peter's boat from Gadara to Capernaum, he said something like that to me. He thanked me for having helped him one day in the Temple in Jerusalem, when actually he had not needed my help at all."

"I believe that he does need us, Claudius. I believe that he needs all men, that he has no other plan for carrying out his purposes. He talked to me for a long time, and when I came away I was happier than I possibly could have been if he had given me a new foot. I hurried back to Elizabeth's. She and some of the other girls were waiting for me. When they heard me coming into the house and could hear the same old thump! thump! thump! they were ready to cry.

"I began to tell them some of the things Jesus had said, and we talked for a long, long time. We were trying to understand why Jesus had left this ugly foot as it was, and this is the decision to which we came. We could not doubt his power to heal, nor his love for me, but we felt that Jesus needed a follower who has a real affliction such as mine. He needed someone who has the faith and the strength to continue as his follower in spite of anything. We decided that he could never establish the kingdom he has come to establish, if the faith the people have in him is dependent solely upon the physical gifts which he gives. We are convinced now that, although he does meet many people on a physical basis and grants petitions for physical healing, unless he also has those who have the courage to accept as a precious gift the quietness of heart which can accompany his refusals, he never can get beyond the appeal which he makes to their own personal gratification."

Susanna leaned over, took her heavy foot in both hands, lifted it a bit from the white sand of the beach, and looked at it. For the first time I could see in her eyes the sorrow of all the years, but only for a moment. "We believe sincerely, Claudius," she said, "that the kind of faith which is going to last, and which is going to change this whole wide world, is the kind which can say to him, 'I believe that you are the Christ, the Son of God, and if you have given me wealth and material things, I thank you from the bottom of my heart, but if you never have, and never will, give me anything but poverty, I will still believe.' Although he sometimes does answer our prayers with a miracle, he needs those who can say, 'If you give me the answer I seek, I will be grateful, but if you must say No to my prayers, or if you must say Wait, until the waiting makes the heart sick, I still will believe and trust you.' "

"I think you are wonderful, Susanna!"

"No, not I, Claudius. This is the faith I found that day I talked with Jesus. Now I walk with pride. I feel that my ugly, grotesque foot is like a badge of honor. I feel that my thump! thump! thump! proves to all the world that my belief in him is something which is not dependent solely upon what he can do for me, but in some degree, upon what I can do for him."

+   +   +

On the day when I had only twenty-four more hours left of my vacation, I decided I ought not to miss my last opportunity to swim in the glistening lake.

It had rained the previous day and after I had finished my swim and was walking on the damp sands curling each toe in a sort of luxurious crunch, I heard a hearty laugh and looked up to see Aunt Thomasina sitting in a comfortable chair enjoying the sunshine and observing my rather foolish behavior with obvious interest.

"Do not be embarrassed!" she called out. "I have done the same thing many times."

I pulled a beach chair near hers, and wrapping my warm robe about me, sat down beside her. "You did not go to the class this morning?" I asked.

"I never go!" she answered positively. "Every time I am here, Susanna tries to drag me to that class, but I am completely uninterested. I feel that they are placing the wrong interpretations on the prophecies when they try to connect them with the young man Jesus. Nor do I approve of my brother's tramping around the country with him."

"I am amazed, Aunt Thomasina!" I said. "I had supposed, without asking, that you believed as the rest of our friends here believe."

"You could not be more mistaken, my boy. I believe the Scriptures. I believe that God will indeed send a deliverer to his people, but I believe he will come in power and in might. He will come in vengeance on those nations who have oppressed, and who are now oppressing us. What this young Jesus needs if he plans to drive the Romans from our land is not a little band of nondescript men like my brother, but strength! He needs religious and political influence! When he ought to be firing men's hearts with ambition for national aggrandizement, he talks to them about loving one another and forgiving the people who despitefully use them.

"Everything in this whole wide world is wrong! Everywhere we see graft and abuse and oppression of the poor, and Jesus goes about healing people who are sick and afflicted!"

"Have you heard him teach, Aunt Thomasina?"

"I have heard him. I have heard him many times. I have stood in the rain to hear him, and the thing which fills me with anger is that he has power! He has strength! He has the ability to fulfill all our hopes, and he dissipates it!"

"Aunt Thomasina, I want to tell you that the first time I saw Jesus it was in the Temple in Jerusalem, and he was driving out great, strong men who were bitterly opposed to him. If you had been there that day, you could never say that he is weak or futile or incapable of being consumed with righteous anger!"

"I find it impossible to imagine, Tribune."

"And Mariamne was telling me only yesterday that she, Susanna, and Matthew had heard Jesus one day as he talked to the people here. He stood in the market place, and she said the words he used were different from any she had ever heard him speak. She said he began to upbraid many here in this city of Capernaum who have scoffed at his words and have failed to repent of the very sins which you mentioned."

"I am gratified to know that anger can stir him. He will never be able to accomplish great things by talking about love and mercy. Stern justice—that is what this world needs!"

"But his words on that day, Mariamne said, were not words of love nor soft or gentle words at all. She said they were searing, scorching words of correction and reproof. He upbraided them because in this city which has been given the greatest opportunity of any city in the world, there are hundreds who have chosen deliberately to ignore his teachings or to reject them.

"I think you are mistaken when you say that Jesus dissipates his potentialities for leadership, or that because he is gentle and

understanding and compassionate, he is weak or ineffective. I
think that though he often has the voice of harpers playing on
their harps, he can also have the voice of thunder."

"My young Greek friend!" said Aunt Thomasina looking at me
intently and smiling. "This is something I had never expected to
hear. A Gentile pleading the case of a Jew, and doing it well
and convincingly too, with a few poetic phrases thrown in for
good measure! Is it possible that you are turning away from
your own obliging gods and goddesses, who, from what I hear,
look the other way when a few polite sins are committed, as long
as they are kept polite and in the best taste?

"Are you, a Greek, a tribune in the army of His Imperial
Majesty, Tiberius Caesar, of the invincible empire of Rome, about
to become a follower of the meek and mild Jesus?"

As Aunt Thomasina tucked her strong hand in the crook of my
arm and we started walking up the beach where the girls stood
waving, I thought to myself that it had been a strange argument
indeed!

+   +   +

The more strict Jewish people broke their fast no earlier than
nine in the morning, and gathered about their tables again only
when the sun was low in the skies, but in Matthew's house the
customs were much the same as in my father's house in Athens.
The meal at noon, however, was a small matter of much in-
formality, a few dates or figs or bunches of purple grapes held in
our hands, with glasses of pomegranate juice, cooled or hot as the
weather demanded, in earthen pitchers, with the glasses nearby.

Today something was different. A servant knocked at my door
to announce with formality, "Your presence is requested in the
peristyle at the hour of noon."

When I could look from my window and no longer see the
spears of bright sunlight piercing the branches of the acacia trees
which bordered the walkway to the great bronze gate to Matthew's estate, I went down the stairs and into the peristyle. Tomorrow I would be leaving Matthew, Susanna, and Mariamne
and returning to the Jerusalem garrison. A sort of faint sadness,
sensed more than actually felt, filled me. I looked out toward

the sea, pensively. The blue waters moved barely at all in the noonday stillness. The monolithic columns of white marble which surrounded the peristyle glistened and sparkled like snow in the sun, and the tall hedges of the showy spacte shrub with its long spikes of orange-colored flowers formed a striking contrast. The outdoor bathing pool had the look of smooth, green marble, and from the small lodge into which the visitors to Matthew's house often overflowed, there was the high, sweet music of a flute, the muffled percussions of a timbrel and the softened twanging of a lute.

Hearing stifled laughter at the top of the stairs, I glanced upward to see Susanna, Mariamne, and Aunt Thomasina marching down like a procession. They were arrayed in their finest tunics of dyed linen embroidered in gold and silver threads and precious stones. They wore white leather sandals, and even Susanna's heavy, clumsy shoe was white and besprinkled with gay stones of red and blue and yellow. She carried a wreath of laurel leaves and flowers such as those placed on the heads of eminent personages in Greece to do them honor, and she placed it, a little awry, upon my own head.

The servant bowed low and ushered me to the seat of honor. He hastened to draw saffron curtains between the columns to shut out the glare of the high-riding sun. Mariamne rose solemnly, as if to make an address, but my wreath slipped crazily upon my nose, and the laughter could be controlled no longer; the pretense was ended. The meal, however, was a festive one. Tall silver compotes held figs and dates and bunches of grapes. There was breast of dove with a spicy sauce made from cummin seeds. There were the choice cheeses from the Tyropoeon Valley in Jerusalem, so famous and widely known that the valley had been given the Greek name meaning valley of the cheese-makers. There were cucumbers with a piquant dressing prepared from the succulent leaves of the leek.

In brass lavers, sweet, pungent incense burned, and a servant moved noiselessly on sandaled feet, sprinkling the perfume of saffron on the gently moving curtains. Multicolored birds in their gilded reed cages made sleepy, chirping noises of love to each other. Mariamne's hair was drawn high on her head and wound about with silver ribbons and long strings of seed pearls. Excitement made her eyes like great, bottomless black pools. Words came into my mind, and I knew not whence they came, whether I had read them or heard them or prayed them in some far distant past. Let mine be the lips which touch her mouth.

Prayed? The unfamiliar word turned itself about in my mind. Martha of Bethany, on the first day I met her, spoke of prayer. "When we heard of your brave deed in saving the child, we called your name in our evening prayers." On the day I left Bethany she had said, "The road to Jericho is dangerous. I will pray God to keep you safe." I wondered if, far back, my ancestors had prayed to Zeus and to Apollo. I wondered about the strong, strange urge toward worship in my heart when my parents had not considered it at all. I wondered at my constantly increasing yearning for strength beyond my own, and for courage and quietness of heart.

As my mind came back to the conversation, I realized that the dejected woman, Joanna, whom I had seen one night in the dreary inn in Gadara, was the subject. Elizabeth, her friend and Peter's mother-in-law, had taken Jesus to the inn to see Joanna. She had not turned away as she had from me, and as Elizabeth had feared she might from Jesus. She had attended the morning class, and she had prayed, not a prayer of petition but of joy and thanksgiving. She had told God, Susanna was saying, how ashamed she was of the wasted years when she had sat in the gloomy inn wrapped in her own commiserations, making of herself an idol at whose feet she knelt in pity. She had become a different woman. Her shoulders had lifted, her hands no longer moved in ceaseless, futile movements, and her beautiful black hair was now smooth and bright.

Even as they related this dramatic change in Joanna in which they felt sincere interest, Mariamne and Susanna could not restrain their delightful sense of the ridiculous. "Mariamne and I used to whisper when we saw her that her hair would make a good home for despondent field mice."

"Girls!" Aunt Thomasina said, reprovingly, but laughing as heartily as the rest. "Perhaps you should tell us what you learned at your study rather than making fun of your elders."

I told myself that Aunt Thomasina wanted to know what took place even though she professed to feel no interest in the class.

"You tell them, Mariamne," suggested Susanna, "you understood it best."

"It was a portion of the prophecy of Isaiah," Mariamne answered—solemn now. "It was the part which says, 'Ho, everyone who thirsts, come to the waters. He who has no money, come, buy and eat!' My father reads it often for what he calls its lofty cadences, but he says Isaiah is often hard to understand. Hearing Jesus teach has made it plain and clear. I think that Isaiah was looking out across the centuries, to this very day and all the days to come. I think it was as if he saw God, no longer limited to a certain nation, or a certain caste, or a certain color; it was as if he saw him limited no longer by education or culture or social, political, or religious prestige, but holding out his great gentle arms to everybody. Perhaps this is the reason Jesus has come to this tiny, smug, self-satisfied corner of the world. Perhaps his purpose is to make plain to us all the things God has tried to get into our tight little minds for centuries gone by. I have heard you say, Claudius, how you and your parents felt concerning your assignment to Palestine. I thought today, as we studied, that in some far greater and infinitely deeper way, somewhere in the eternal councils of God, the same assignment had been handed to Jesus—Palestine.

"Perhaps God has sent his own son to this little land, endeavoring to show us what he is like, and what he purposes for the world. Perhaps he wants us to learn that God is not for our people alone. Perhaps he is showing us that he is not a God to be wrapped and hidden in the vestments of any nation's priesthood. Perhaps he wants us to look at Jesus and through him to see a God who longs to reconcile himself to all the wistful, seeking people in the whole wide world."

As the four of us walked out onto the front court, we saw a man running down the street toward Matthew's house. When he came near, I saw that it was Alexander, the loved servant of Centurion Ananelus, and when he handed me a note, I was distressed to find that the old soldier had grown quite ill, and was urging me to come to him immediately. I had a high esteem for Ananelus, both because of his courage in deserting the gods of his youth and clinging to the God who satisfied his heart, and for having used his own money to build for the Jews of Capernaum a far more complete synagogue than they could have built for themselves.

He was lying quietly on his couch, entirely conscious and seemingly without pain. "Thank you for coming, my son," he said to me, "it is only when one is very old and dying that one has a right to make demands upon youth."

"Not at all, sir,'" I answered. "I wanted very much to see you."

"I have an important favor to ask, and I must speak quickly. I have told you how dear my servant Alexander is to me, and I have prepared a legal article giving him his freedom. Knowing, however, the graft which transpires in Rome concerning slaves, he will need a sponsor to help and to advise. You will take care of this matter for me?"

"I will indeed, sir. You need have no qualms either about his safety or his freedom."

Ananelus smiled faintly. "You forget your rank, Tribune; a superior officer does not address a centurion as 'sir.' "

I reached down and took the wrinkled old hand of Ananelus in my own. "You are correct, Centurion," I agreed, "but there never can be a question of rank between us. Goodbye, sir."

Outside in the street in front of the house, the professional mourners, sensing the smell of death in the air, had already gathered. They were prepared, for a price, to begin their weeping and wailing, beating on their breasts and gnashing their teeth. As they waited, they were listening to a man who seemed not to be one of them.

"I was there," he told them, "on the day when Jesus healed this centurion's servant. It was the day he healed me. Do you know what it means to be a leper? It is like no other illness. You have an incurable disease. You are waiting to die.

"Other people, declared beyond hope by the physicians, lie on their couches in their own homes. Their loved ones gather about them. They bring cool cloths to place on a fevered brow. They prepare their choicest and most nourishing foods. Friends come in and touch their hands to give them courage.

"Not when you are a leper! You must leave your family. You must stay outside the city in a camp where there are only those who have the same loathsome disease. No one can touch you! Do you know what that means? No one can touch you! When there is the necessity for you to go where there are other people, you must go with your head uncovered. You must call out constantly the searing, monotonous, humiliating words, 'Unclean! Unclean! Unclean!' They come to be like a deep, rugged furrow in your brain. Sometimes at night you waken yourself screaming them at the top of your voice.

"There was a tremendous crowd around Jesus that day, and I knew I had no right to be there. Even though I stood on the very edge of the crowd, people began to point at me, to call out, 'Go away, leper, go away!' They drew their robes tightly around their legs.

"But I had heard the authority in Jesus' voice. His clothes were the clothes of a peasant. He wore no phylacteries, nor was there any broadening of the borders of his garment such as were worn by the dignitaries from the Temple in Jerusalem. I did not know from what source his authority would come, but I was convinced of his power. I knew he could heal me, but I was afraid. I was afraid he might join the others and call out, 'Go away, leper!'

"As he came down the mountainside near the place where I stood, I had one sudden burst of courage. I called out to him, 'Lord, if you will, you can make me clean!' He heard me. He put out his hand and touched me. You cannot know what it meant. No one had touched me for a long, long time. The hot tears coursed down my cheeks. I looked at my hands. I touched my face. I tore open my robe and looked at my body. I was well. I was a man again. I began to run. Remembering the tenderness of my wife's soft, red lips. Remembering the tenderness of soft arms about my strong, healthy body. Remembering the touch of baby hands. Most of all, remembering Jesus."

The door to Ananelus' house opened, and Alexander came out

wiping his eyes and trying to control his trembling voice. Centurion Ananelus was dead. The crowd turned away from the man who had been a leper, and began to weep and to wail.

+   +   +

The messenger I sent to Caesarea to inform Pilate of the death of the centurion returned after a short time. Pilate's communication told me that since there was no officer available to take charge of the Capernaum fort and since replacements from Rome were usually sent out in the spring, he wished to have me remain in Galilee for the winter.

He added that the house in which Ananelus had lived was the property of the Roman government and that if I wished to take up residence there, I would have his approval. I was eager to take advantage of his offer, but since I had no aide in Capernaum, I dismissed the matter from my mind as impracticable.

After I had gone to the fort, however, to report to the soldiers concerning the delay in replacing their officer, I decided that I must not forget my promise to Ananelus and that I must find Alexander and determine with him what plans ought to be made for his new-found liberty. I was both surprised and delighted to find he did not wish to be free, that he had no ambition to become a citizen. He assured me a little tearfully that if I would let him stay and perform the same duties for me that he had undertaken for his late master, his life would be complete once more.

It was a wonderful winter, there in Capernaum of Galilee. Mariamne was spending much of the time now with Susanna, and every time she was making preparations for a stay in Jerusalem, I felt more certain that the joys of any season or of any place would be insipid and meaningless without her.

She told us that her father now spent much time searching the Scriptures when not engaged in teaching or in the law. A friend, she said, one Joseph of Arimathea, stayed sometimes for a week in the town-house of Nicodemus, and together they would pore over the ancient writings until late at night, and begin discussing them as soon as they came to breakfast in the mornings.

Since both of them were members of the Sanhedrin, she said, they were fearful for Jesus and for anyone who might be found believing in him.

For months I had thought that I had never seen a man so happy or so satisfied as Matthew. Sometimes, however, I had seen a troubled frown appear, and for a long time he would be strangely quiet. When Mariamne suggested that her father felt that trouble was brewing, Susanna spoke to Matthew about it.

"Surely he must be mistaken," she said, her face suddenly white and stricken.

"No, my child," Matthew answered. "Everywhere we go now, we see them standing around in small, but determined, purposeful groups—the Pharisees, the Sadducees, the Herodians, the scribes—trying to trap Jesus with their questions. Jairus tells me that they have dared to hold a council here in Capernaum in our own synagogue, with the avowed purpose of endeavoring to find a way to destroy him. We realize that their hatred and fear of him have gone far beyond arguing and criticism. I fear that from now on it is going to be a matter of organized planning to bring a man to death."

"Father!" Susanna cried, "how can you say such a thing?"

"It is true, my dear one," Matthew said. "There has already been an edict issued by the Sanhedrin which forbids his going into the city of Jerusalem and which threatens any person in Jerusalem found believing in him with excommunication."

"I cannot understand it," I told them. "I cannot understand why those influential people who are the religious as well as the political leaders of Palestine want to destroy Jesus. Surely they must know that thousands of people love him and are made better and happier because of him. There is nothing of which they can legally accuse him. Perhaps you are overly apprehensive, sir. Reputable persons do not set about to cause the death of an innocent man."

"I wish I could agree with you, my son," Matthew said sadly. "It is possible that the very fact you mention concerning the love of the multitudes for him is their reason for hating him. We must remember that for many years these men are the ones who have made the rules, and they have made them for their own advantage. They are the ones who have been followed and obeyed.

"For almost two years now, Jesus has been holding up their spurious piety for all the people to see, and the leaders are consumed with fear that the populace is beginning to discern, however slowly, that this organization of religion to which they hold has long since become a moribund, decadent thing. They are terrified that Jesus may indeed be the open door to a completely new order which will be free to everyone and in which they—the important ones—will be forced to sit in seats no higher than the simplest of his followers. Do not be mistaken about them, Claudius. These men wield a power beyond anything you can possibly conceive."

Party of Horror

All too soon, it seemed, the rigorous Galilean winter was over, and although I was glad for the bright sunshine sparkling on the blue waters of the Sea of Galilee, and glad to hear the children playing in the streets and the vendors shouting their wares, I felt sure that my stay in Capernaum must be near an end. I remembered that it was usually in April that replacements were sent out from Rome, and each day I expected to hear from Pilate that a centurion was on his way to take the place of Ananelus.

As I was lying lazily in bed one morning, my mind went back to the April day, two years ago, when I myself had been sent as a replacement for one of the tribunes in the Jerusalem garrison.

I remembered how my mother and father and I had felt on the day when I left Athens. We had thought that I was going to the very end of the world, that the people would be of some strange and unknown variety, as different from our own friends and acquaintances as if the same earth did not hold us. We felt that the three years ahead were to be years of punishment for each of us.

I wondered if they could ever picture this land as it really was. I wondered whether they would ever be able to picture Nicodemus as a man equal in fine traditions, education, mental attainments, and legal sagacity to my own father. I wondered if they could conceive of his wife as possessing charm and grace equal to that of my own mother and her friends. I thought of Susanna, her attractiveness in spite of her heavy, clumsy, misshapen foot.

I wondered most of all if they could begin to realize the quiet beauty and the shining wonder of a girl like Mariamne.

When Alexander knocked on my door, he had something to add to his usual morning greeting. "You had best hurry a bit, sir," he said. "You have a guest from Jerusalem who will be joining you."

Hastening with my dressing, I tried to think who could be calling on me from Jerusalem at this early hour. The name of Tribune Julius, the conqueror from Rome, did not enter my mind. When I caught sight of him, however, standing at the foot of the stairs, I felt mildly pleased to see him again, although I remembered in a flash the contradictory attitudes he always presented.

I had not forgotten how, after holding forth with evident feeling against the Jews in general, he had seemed to enjoy recounting for me large portions of their history and their prophecies. I recalled vividly my amazement when I had questioned him about Jesus, how he had answered with sincerity that even though Jesus was a Jew, one did not hate him, and that even though he was a man—and more—one was not jealous of him.

Alexander, with his usual thoughtfulness, had prepared the breakfast with extra care, but as we ate I noticed that Julius was only toying with his food and that he looked wan and much unlike the round-faced, rosy-cheeked young man I remembered.

He talked almost constantly but in a desultory manner, mentioning the other tribunes by name, telling their present whereabouts, saying that Zoldi was coming more and more to believe in the Jewish God and spending most of his extra time listening to the Jewish Scriptures as they were read in the Temple. He talked about the weather in Jerusalem and about his tiring journey. I could discern, however, that he was distraught and was not saying the things which were on his mind.

Finally, he seemed to exert a great effort to collect his thoughts. "You must forgive me, Lysias," he said, "I had almost forgotten to tell you of my reason for coming to Capernaum. I have a communication sent by Pontius Pilate. If you hate to plow through his bombastic ramblings as much as I do, I can tell you what it is he wishes you to do."

He placed his hands against his temples, and pressed them hard. "A number of notables from Jerusalem, Pilate himself heading the list, are planning to travel to Tiberias in a few days and together with some important persons in the northern province, to give a surprise party for Herod on his birthday. He is extending an invitation to you and he wishes to use this opportunity to discuss the plans he has made for you to leave Capernaum. He has decided that you should now revisit the tax-collectors whom you investigated earlier in order to determine whether any improvements in their methods have been put into effect before definite plans are made to relieve them of their positions."

Even as Julius was telling me these things, I could see that he was preoccupied, and I felt a growing concern for him. Though he seemed to be using much of Pilate's own manner of speech, he stopped often in the middle of a sentence as if he found it difficult to remember what he was saying.

"Lysias," he blurted out suddenly, "I am not a popular man. I never have been. Even when I was a boy, although I wanted to be liked, I seemed always to have an uncanny ability to discern the weak points in any person I met, and I could not resist taking a deep probe into that vulnerable spot if any opportunity presented itself."

For a brief moment he smiled and looked more as I had remembered him. "When you yourself first came to join the tribunes in Jerusalem, I knew immediately that you considered yourself above most of us in background and education, and the fact that you spoke often of your father and mother let me see that you did not have the hard, calloused approach to life that one finds in most soldiers, particularly officers."

The momentary smile was gone as he added, "At first I hated you for those things and struck out at you whenever I could. You had all the things I always had wanted—kindness, understanding, even a family to be proud of—and I had nothing. I had thought that if I could get away from the kind of home I had in Rome, come to a foreign country, and live among officers of my own rank, I would learn how to make friends. I was wrong. The officers in the tower avoided me, and I cannot blame them as my caustic tongue does not make me a pleasant companion."

Julius stopped again to press his hands hard against his

temples. "I am desperate now, Claudius Lysias, for someone to talk to. You used to listen to me in Jerusalem, and it was because I remembered and thought you might listen to me now that I inveigled Pilate into permitting me to bring the communication."

I was more than ready to concede that Julius needed a friend, but whatever his problems were, I felt that any advice and help I might be able to give would not be enough. I assured him, however, that if talking would be a help and there were things he wished to discuss, I certainly would be more than glad to listen.

He seemed almost pitiful in his gratitude as he began to talk.

"I think you will remember, Lysias," he said, "that I told you in Jerusalem how the tribunes—and even the common soldiers —made veiled remarks about Salome, judging her by her exotic beauty, the torrid dances her mother forces her to dance, and the attentions she must accept from her stepfather Herod in public places."

"I remember, Julius," I told him hesitantly, remembering also Zoldi's widely divergent opinion.

I wished I could tell Julius now that Zoldi had described this girl, who was so chaste and guileless in his eyes, as a woman unable to resist drawing every man with whom she came in contact into her net and using whatever means seemed feasible at the moment. I wanted to help him, but I feared that any reference to Salome's true character might throw him into a display of temper which could result disastrously for us both.

I made one small effort. "Perhaps Salome is only excited and upset when she complains of her mother's demands," I suggested. "It is possible she exaggerates the things she tells you."

"She does not!" Julius stated positively with his old belligerent attitude. "She hates the lewd dances and the veils. She hates and fears her mother who forces her to appear as something which she is not. I know and understand Salome, and I must take her away."

He rose from his chair, walked to the decanter on a nearby table and poured himself a glass of wine, drinking it in great gulps.

"All last night," he said, "I walked the floor, and I have come to a decision. Tribune Lysias, I have decided to resign my office as tribune. I realize quite well what such a step will do to my career and to my life. I know that Pilate will see to it that my resignation is reported as a dishonorable discharge and that I will never be able to obtain a position of any description either in Palestine or in Rome."

I was aghast at what this man was about to do. I felt that I must dare remonstrate. "Julius, my friend," I said to him in all earnestness, "this is a tremendous decision you are making. Your entire future is at stake."

"I have one thing in my favor," he said. "Although we have no standing in Rome, we have money. I also have a large inheritance from my grandmother which is available to me in its entirety at any time. Salome and I would be poor, but we can live all our lives in decency and in the happiness which she deserves. We have considered the matter carefully. She plans for me to get my inheritance and leave the entire sum with her until I can travel to some distant land and arrange to send for her."

"Are you certain this is what you want?"

"I love Salome, Lysias. I am torn with love of her. What else can I do?"

"Are you sure she will come to you?"

I had gone too far! I was barely able to move fast enough to escape the impact of his fist against my face. Immediately he was repentant.

"Forgive me, Lysias," he said, holding his hands against his closed eyes. "You are my only friend, and I can not bear to have you doubt Salome. I am sure that she will come to me. We have perfected all our plans. This is what we will do. I shall attend this detestable birthday party so that Pilate will suspect nothing until he finds my resignation when he returns to Caesarea. I know how things will be. I have attended affairs in the palace of Tetrarch Herod in Tiberias before. When all the guests are dull with wine, Salome and I will slip into the courtyard to say our goodbyes. It will not be long until she joins me. I can wait."

All that day after Julius had gone, and late into the night, I was troubled and distressed. I considered going to Susanna

and Matthew and asking their opinion concerning what course
I should follow, but I did not like to betray Julius' confidence
in me. I wished I could hear what Mariamne would say.

In my mind I was certain that nothing could ever change
Julius until his heart was broken. I wished he would not go to
the party. I wished many things, and as the day on which I was
to travel to Tiberias drew near, I grew more and more apprehensive.

On the morning when I started across the lake, I was tense
and restless. By the time the boat was in sight of the impressive
city which Herod had built for himself, it had begun to rain.
It was one of those cold spring rains which seem interminable.
The dark waves beating against the sides of the boat intensified
my forebodings.

Fortunately for me, we docked at Herod's private landing
which was only a short distance from the rear of the palace, and
since a servant stood waiting with an extra coat, I was able to
arrive in the great banquet hall in some semblance of order.

It did not take me longer than the time to glance around the
room to see that no matter in what degree of dress or undress I
had presented myself, it would have meant less than nothing
to the people assembled there.

I was surprised at the large number who had come up from
Jerusalem and from other parts of Judea as well as those from
the northern parts of Palestine. They were all arrayed in the
most elegant costumes and were wearing expensive jewelry. I
supposed that in their less abandoned moments they were men
and women of the aristocratic class, substantial citizens of this
country. They stood around now, however, with glassy looks in
their watery eyes, holding glasses of wine in their hands. Most
of the men and women had their arms around each other, and
here and there, lolling upon a couch, a man would pull one
of the women down upon his knees.

The music was loud and exciting. Occasionally one of the
women, her drink in her hand, would maneuver a space in the
center of the floor and would begin to engage in some sort of
gyrations which by some stretch of the imagination might be
called a dance. Sometimes one of the men would push his way out

to where she was, seize her in his arms, and together they would continue their revolting undulations.

These people were not young. I felt sure that many of them were much older than my own parents, and while I was not a novice at attending parties where there was drinking and where some of the behavior was far from restrained, those affairs had been attended by people who were my fellow-students or those who were near my own age and were understandably irresponsible.

My mother and father and their friends, while they were far from prudish, nevertheless behaved with a dignity and decorum which I had come to associate with maturity. As I watched these men and women, I had the feeling that I ought to turn my face away in shame, not for myself but for them.

I reminded myself, however, that all over Palestine there were people like Nicodemus and Matthew and their families who would have considered this sort of behavior repellent.

It did not take much imagination for me to picture how it was that the party had turned into an orgy so early in the evening. I knew that most of the crowd probably had traveled together from Jerusalem and that by the time they had reached Herod's palace and were ready to shout their birthday greetings, they were well on their way to their present condition.

Except for the fact that I feared for Julius and still held the hope that there might be a way I could help him or even dissuade him from his tragic decision, and that I reminded myself that I was here under orders from my superior officer, Pontius Pilate, I think I should have been inclined to go out into the rain, walk to the dock, and set sail in any boat going to Capernaum.

Before much time had elapsed, Pilate caught sight of me and elbowed his way through the crowd to the place where I was standing. He threw his arm about my shoulders and shouted above the music and the laughter.

"Get you a drink, my boy! Can't enjoy the party without a drink! Got to talk to you! Important business! Get you a drink!"

Much to my relief, he caught sight of someone more interesting, and moved away as if he had forgotten me completely.

After what seemed to me an almost interminable period, the

servants began to bring in great trays of all kinds of exotic foods. The glasses were collected, and the crowd moved half-heartedly toward the banquet table. As far as I could tell, however, they were totally uninterested in the display of food and concerned only with having the glasses which were on the table filled so that they might begin the whole process over again.

Far down the table, at such a distance that I scarcely could distinguish her features, I saw Salome sitting beside her mother.

I had an intense curiosity about this girl. I had seen her only the one time when I attended Pilate's supper party on the night of my arrival in Jerusalem, and at that time I had been concerned only with her beauty and her evident talent for the kind of dance which she was performing. Now I was eager to see her as a person and endeavor to reconcile the completely diverse opinions of her which I had heard from Julius and from Zoldi.

Julius had seemed so convinced of her goodness and sincerity that I tried to console myself by thinking that Zoldi, being an older man, had misjudged Salome or had been too hasty in forming judgment from things which might have been exaggerated. Perhaps, I had been telling myself for the last hour, Julius was right and the whole affair would turn out for his happiness.

As my eyes became accustomed to the dim light, I tried to search the expression on Salome's exquisitely beautiful face, and although I was able to discern the ease with which she had been able to make the infatuated Julius believe in her youth and innocence, I could see the hard lines around her mouth which portrayed a determination to squeeze life as one might squeeze a piece of fruit until it lay flat and flaccid in one's hands.

I wondered if it were possible that under the influence of a ruthless, ambitious mother, she was a girl who somehow had lost her way, and that Julius was able to see the girl she might have been. I wondered if the pedestal of innocence upon which the young tribune had placed her might have represented a long-dead, secret aspiration.

Once again, however, I reminded myself of Zoldi's carefully guarded description as he spoke of a member of the household of Herod. "Salome takes her male companionship where she finds it."

When the servants came in to remove the plates before serving the dessert, Herod suddenly stood up and began to clap his hands.

"Quiet, everybody!" he shouted. "What we need is entertainment! I must do something to show my appreciation for this fine gesture of yours! I will have my beautiful stepdaughter dance for you! Go quickly, my pet, and don the veils I had made for you in Egypt! Do you not also wish to show your appreciation?"

I looked at Julius, and I was filled with apprehension. His round face was drawn into lines of hatred which made my blood run cold. His once rosy cheeks were as white as death itself, and his childish mouth was set in a hard, straight line.

If I could have moved from my seat without attracting attention to him, I would have gone to him and made some effort to quiet the murderous look I could see in his eyes. Even as I wished to help him, however, I knew the hopelessness of such an effort. If only I could have taken him to Jesus, I thought to myself.

Suddenly there was a fanfare of trumpets such as I had heard on that night in Jerusalem. Salome came slowly into the room. She was clad in the filmy white costume I had seen before, and she began to dance with an abandon which caused the veils to drop to the floor, one after another, until her small but exquisitely formed body was revealed as if she wore no clothes at all.

As she passed near where Julius was seated, she came almost to a stop. For a brief moment, I thought perhaps she meant to single him out for some show of favor, but with a gloating look of accomplishment on her face, she pressed her forefinger against the center of her thumb, and carelessly—almost insultingly— flipped a lock of his hair.

I saw the blood rush to his face and the look of consternation in his eyes. I knew without being told that Salome already had the inheritance Julius had promised her. I knew without doubt that Salome was finished with Julius.

Herod was standing with his bulging, reddened eyes fixed on the girl's beautiful body. He gulped down a full glass of wine, and then he began to shout. His words were so befuddled, and the music so loud, that at first I could not make out what he was saying. Soon one of the guests ran out onto the floor, signaled for the music-makers to stop, seized Salome by the arm, and pulled her over to the place where Herod was standing.

"Listen to him!" he screamed, shaking her by the shoulders. "Listen to what he is offering you! He wants to give you something! Ask for something big!"

Salome had a hard, fixed smile on her face as if it were painted there. I wondered if she was remembering the fortune which already had been given her that very evening by a boy who loved her and who thought she meant to follow him to distant lands and become his wife.

Herodias, although obviously as drunk as the others, had not failed to take in the situation at a glance. This was something for which she had waited, and she was not forgetting for one hour the humiliation and hatred which had gnawed at her heart so long.

It was common knowledge that she had persuaded Herod to have John the Baptist brought from Machaerus and placed in a dungeon under the palace in Tiberias so that every torture which her fertile mind could devise might be added to his sufferings. She pulled Salome down, and began to whisper frantically in her ear.

Herod was reeling back and forth in front of his chair. "Ask for anything!" he shouted. "Ask for the half of my kingdom!"

The drunken fool, I thought to myself, he has no kingdom. But those who at that moment were no better able to judge kingdoms than Herod himself were shouting, "Take it! Take it! Take half of his kingdom!"

It was Herodias who stood up now, pounding on the table for attention.

"Listen to me, everybody!" she screamed, her face ravaged with vengeance. "Salome knows what she wants! She knows what it is for which she wishes to ask."

I could see the thin clawlike fingers of her hand pressed into Salome's soft arm.

In the moments which passed before she answered, I supposed that Salome was going to satisfy the ambitions of Herodias and make both of them wealthy for life. I did not doubt for one moment that she would ask for half of Herod's money and lands.

When she spoke, her words were so low that I could barely hear them, and when I did, it was as if I was in the midst of a terrifying dream from which I must awake before the terror became a reality.

"The head of John the Baptist here on a platter!"

My mind could not assimilate the words I heard. I sat numb and still. Even the drunken crowd had become quiet. From far down the table a few of the guests were saying weakly, "No! Herodias! No!"

In the place of honor beside the babbling Herod, Pilate sat bolt upright. For a moment I thought he might be planning to terminate this horrible thing which seemed to be gathering momentum. But Pilate's eyes were distended in surprise and disbelief, and he was waving his right hand aimlessly back and forth. He looked at the great gold and amethyst ring as if he expected it to show some authority in this unexpected and tragic development.

"She has asked now!" Herodias was shrieking. "You all heard what Herod promised! Anything, he said. Anything!"

A few of the more drunken ones were joining her and shouting also. "Come on, Herod!" they shouted. "Send for the executioner! Let him go down into the dungeon and bring up the preacher's head! Let us see how it will look beside the fatted calf! Let us show everybody what will happen if they dare to criticize the people who are in power in this land."

Herod assumed an attitude of drunken dignity. "I have given my oath," he said. "Send for the executioner, servant! Take this silver platter! Do not return with it empty!"

It was horrible. When the servant returned, I would not look. I did not see the spectacle which turned their faces white and drained their driveling lips of color.

Herod was no longer arrogant. He was on his feet drinking glass after glass of wine as if he wanted to dull his mind completely to the thing he had done. Suddenly he seized Salome. He threw his arms around her, and began to drag her toward the door into the courtyard.

"Come my pet," he was saying as he passed my seat. "You have your wish! You must repay me!"

It is raining, I said to myself.

Looking down the table, I saw the face of Julius, the expression startlingly like the expression I had seen in Zoldi's room almost two years ago when he had said of the Jews, "I could kill them all," and I had known that he meant it. I could see that now he knew what he intended to do.

He was following Herod and Salome into the courtyard, and as quickly as I could, I pushed my way through the crowd which was beginning to try desperately to get away from the horror on the table. When I reached the outer door, I saw that Pontius Pilate was ahead of me.

When I finally came into Herod's beautiful courtyard, Julius was dead.

He lay face down in the mud. A servant had reached him and was saying, "A terrible accident, Tribune! He must have tripped and have fallen on his sword! You will report it as an accident, sir, I am sure."

I stooped down, and turned Julius over. I saw the blood gushing from the wound in his side, but I saw something else as well. There was mud on his white, boyish face, but plainly discernible on his temple was the imprint of a heavy gold ring.

I understood what had happened as plainly as if I had seen it for myself. Pilate would have cared nothing had he seen his old enemy Herod lying dead, but he could not risk a scandal in the Roman army of which he was in command.

"Poor Julius," Zoldi had said on that evening which seemed so long ago. "Poor Julius," I whispered as I turned away.

When I awoke the next morning after only two or three hours of fitful sleep, I had only one desire and that was to depart from Herod's opulent estate as quickly as I could find a boat sailing toward Capernaum. I could hear the rain, still falling steadily on the roof, and although I had made every effort to put the events of the previous evening out of my mind, I could not keep from wondering if Julius' body still lay in the mud in Herod's courtyard.

I dreaded going down the stairs for fear that some of the horror of last night's debacle might remain, and I was determined, if possible, to be well on my way back to Capernaum before my host or any of the guests were awake. As I had brought little in the way of luggage, I had begun to tiptoe my way down when I saw, standing at the bottom of the stairs in the attitude of a guard, the same servant who had spoken to me in the courtyard the night before. He stepped aside when I reached the bottom step, saluted as if he were a soldier, and said politely, but with an accusing connotation in his voice, "Good morning, sir. I fear you did not sleep well. You are up quite early."

"I need to get back to Capernaum."

"There is a boat about to sail now, sir. I have engaged passage for you."

"How did you know I would be leaving?"

He looked at me coldly, flicking a speck of dust from his sleeve, and answered, "I fancied you did not imbibe as freely as the others last night, and that you might awaken earlier than they. I wish to remind you again, sir, that you are to report the regrettable death of the tribune as an accident, and that you are not to participate in any unnecessary conversation concerning the sudden and unavoidable death of the prisoner, John the Baptist."

"Unavoidable!" I gasped.

I was irked by the decidedly dictatorial attitude of superiority which this servant was assuming. I had barely glanced at him last night, and so far had given him only a cursory look as he had stopped me this morning, but after his surprising manner, I began to observe him with some curiosity.

He was a rather small, slight man of about fifty, and I noticed that his uniform was extremely ornate for that of a servant. I almost imagined that he wore a breastplate and a bronze helmet with red plumes. I was repelled by the cold, uncompromising stare which seemed to miss looking at me, and still managed to look through me. Although I was eager to be on my way, I could not resist speaking to him further.

"What is your name, my man?" I asked.

"Chuza is my name, Tribune Lysias, and I am Herod's chief steward."

"You seem to have unusual authority."

"I have almost unlimited authority. I have been with Tetrarch Herod for many years, and I enjoy his complete confidence."

There flashed across my mind suddenly a vivid picture of a woman with unkempt black hair, stooped shoulders, and a habit of wringing her hands together as if in sorrow. I had seen her one night in a dreary inn in Gadara.

"I think I know your wife," I said.

"My wife?"

"Joanna."

"Oh yes!" he answered with insulting carelessness. "I have seen her so seldom, and have come to associate with people so entirely different from the provincial class of Capernaum that I often forget that I ever had any connection with them."

"They are wonderful people, Chuza. It is too bad you have had to lose touch with them."

"That, sir, is a matter of opinion."

The insufferable little snob, I thought to myself. What a regrettable waste of love and loyalty and loneliness has been expended upon him.

"I will show you to your boat now, Tribune Lysias." He spoke sternly now, and with great emphasis. "Let me remind you again, the sooner you forget the unfortunate occurrences of last evening, the better."

I did not want to continue my conversation with him, but I could not resist answering.

"I shall not forget them, Chuza. But if you are saying that I am not to try to do anything to bring about the retribution which those events deserve, you can rest assured that I realize fully that I should have no possible chance to prove a case against the Tetrarch of Galilee or against the Roman procurator."

"You are correct, sir, you would not."

When we were halfway across the lake, the sky began to lighten, and by the time I could make out the glistening dome of the synagogue which the beloved Ananelus had built for the people, the sun was shining. I drew a deep breath of relief. It was almost as if I were sailing into a different world.

I wished that I might have seen Aunt Thomasina at that moment when my heart was full. I wished I might have said to her, "I know that you are wrong! It is not power, nor might, nor military strength which this world needs. It is not armies, nor weapons, nor chariots, nor horses, nor any of the accouterments of power. Those things can bring only distrust of one nation for another, and distrust of one people for another. They can bring only a continuing race for greater and greater armies and more and more destructive weapons until there will be no remedy, and no nation and no people will dare to call a halt.

"These are not the things we need! We need the remedy which lies in the hands of the person to whom you refer as the meek and mild Jesus. It is conceivable that the day will finally come which will find weapons so terrifying that all civilizations could be wiped off the earth because no one will have dared to cease his continuing search.

"Perhaps then we, or others like us—the stupid, the slow of heart to believe, the determined ones—will witness events which may cause us to ask ourselves what was so wrong with the precepts Jesus tried to teach. We may wish to ask ourselves what was so wrong with loving one's neighbor more than we love ourselves. We may want to ask what was wrong with meekness and mildness, but we will have no breath with which to ask!"

Miracle on the Green Plains of Bethsaida

As soon as the boat docked, I hurried to the house of Matthew. I was bitterly disappointed to find that only the servants were there.

The man who opened the door held it open only a little way and did not ask me to enter. When I questioned him, he said that the disciples of John the Baptist had come before dawn to find Jesus and to tell him of the death of their leader. I wondered how they could have known so quickly. Jesus had been sad, he told me, and had taken Matthew and the other men and had set off in a northeasterly direction in Peter's boat. He thought they might have gone to Bethsaida-Julias across the lake. The young ladies had been sent to Jerusalem.

I asked if the men who had brought the news about John's death had told them about the death of Tribune Julius. I saw the fear that blanched his face. Danger, like a black, lowering cloud, seemed descending upon him and upon me as he pushed the door almost closed.

"I know nothing, sir," he declared emphatically. "Nothing!"

At the house of Ananelus, I found an additional message to the one which had been brought by Julius. I looked at the one he had brought, and touched it—almost sadly. A palmer worm, wasn't it, that Zoldi had called him, wandering from place to place like a pilgrim. I had never liked Julius. I wondered how his death could make me sad. Poor Julius, I thought.

Pilate's second message, evidently composed and dispatched hurriedly, said that I was to leave Capernaum at once. He wished to have me investigate the advisability of consolidating some of the smaller forts in the northern part of Palestine. It occurred to me that his real reason might have been to have me in provinces where the death of John the Baptist would not be discussed and the death of a Roman tribune would be a matter for congratulation.

His reasons did not interest me greatly. Mariamne and Susanna were no longer in Capernaum. Jesus and Matthew had left on a boat sailing toward Bethsaida-Julias. I wanted to go. Anywhere. I wanted work to drive from my mind the incessant, insistent re-living of scenes hard to forget. I did not want to think of Herod's loose lips or his sensuous, hungry eyes. I did not want to think of the hate and vengeance on the stark face of Herodias. I could not bear to imagine what the horror had been on the silver platter. I did not want to think of the mud on the round, white boyish face of Julius.

As I traveled northward, spring was just beginning to touch the countryside. The myrtle trees were putting out their green leaves, and the almond trees were white and pink against the blue sky. The tall pomegranate trees, often twelve or fifteen feet high, tossed their scarlet petaled flowers in the warm breeze.

In the pastures, goats and sheep, tended by the same shepherd, grazed side by side, the sheep nibbling at the grass and tender leaves while the goats stretched their necks in a determined and businesslike manner to reach for the shrubs and stubborn twigs.

I could see farmers with their plows drawn by two bullocks. As they turned up the sod or harvested their wheat, they sang. Sometimes I stopped to listen in the shade of a terebinth tree while my horse rested. "The fig tree puts forth its figs, and the vines are in blossom; they give forth fragrance . . . . Awake, O north wind, and come, O south wind. Blow upon my garden."

The young men had a different song. "Behold, you are beautiful, my love . . . . Your two breasts are like two fawns, twins of a gazelle, that feed among the lilies."

I listened, and I thought of Ananelus, listening when he was a young soldier. Ananelus was dead. I wished people did not have to die. I wondered what Jesus meant when he told Nicodemus that whoever believed in him should have everlasting life. Ananelus was dead, and Julius was dead. I was sad. I clucked to my horse and started riding.

In some of the fields women were helping the men as they beat the cummin plants with rods to detach the seeds. I called to ask why. The men told me that the women used the seeds to make spices and relish. The women did not raise their heads or answer. They did not trust Roman soldiers.

I often passed fields where cultivation had been neglected and where the nettles had taken over and waved arrogantly in the soft winds. I knew that the sluggard, taking his ease, would soon find that they had conquered his little world.

As arrogant as the nettles, I sometimes saw a rooster marching along, followed by his harem of admiring hens, glancing up with insolence at the black-winged kite gliding noiselessly through the air. The rooster was not so brave as he pretended to be. He knew that the kite was only looking down to see what offal might have been preserved in the winter snows and that he was too cowardly to attack live birds or poultry. But the hens did not know.

The investigation for Pilate concerning the consolidation of the northern forts was a tedious job. The summer went by, dry, hot, and dull.

I came to the last town on my itinerary and drew a long breath of relief. Caesarea Philippi, a romantically beautiful resort town at the northern tip of Palestine, was situated at the source of the Jordan River and was surrounded by hills on all except the western side. To the north, majestic Mount Hermon towered more than nine thousand feet. Capped with snow the year around, the long, feathery, white furrows made their tortuous descent to the valleys below, and I could imagine the Greek god Pan blowing on his pipes and leaping over the crevasses on his goat-like legs. The town had originally been called Paneas, and had a fine white marble temple built by Herod the Great and dedicated to the gods of flocks and herds and patron of the shepherds.

The season was about at an end, and accommodations were readily available. The inn in which I was able to find a room was quite different from the nondescript ones in which I had spent most of my nights. Usually the best I could find was a mud hut with rushes spread on the floor where one could sleep if he wished.

If one desired, he might rent a thin, well-worn mattress redolent of the bodies of many a weary traveler. I always preferred the less comfortable, but more fragrant, grasses.

The inn in Caesarea Philippi, the inn-keeper informed me with great pride, was the one used by Tetrarch Herod and his family. Herod and his brother Philip, Tetrarch of Ituraea, often met there for a few days to discuss private matters. The inn-keeper smiled slyly and added that of course Herod came often in the summer with beautiful ladies whose names he did not write upon the register.

White stone walls surrounded a quadrangular court, and while the sun was warm, I sat on a bench beside a picturesque well which was in the center. Inside, I found the rooms were well scrubbed and the walls whitened with lime.

I finished unpacking enough of my belongings to settle down for a few days before I started my southward journey toward Jerusalem. I stood at the deep-set window and looked out. The light from the setting sun made the grass and the trees a more vivid green and threw a kind of misty rainbow over the peak of Mount Hermon. I wished for Mariamne. I wondered. Would the time ever come when we could stand together at a window, looking out, without the need of words between us?

There was a knock on the door. My friend Matthew stood outside. The ardor of my welcome must have embarrassed him. I threw my arms about him as if he had been my own father.

Question after question tumbled from my lips. It was only when he held up both arms saying, "Wait a minute!" that I realized I had been pouring out queries about where he had been, how he happened to be in Caesarea Philippi, about Mariamne and Susanna, about Jesus.

When we were seated, he told me that the girls had been in Jerusalem with Nicodemus for almost six months, that he had not been willing to leave them in Capernaum even with the servants and Aunt Thomasina. There was danger, he said, to everyone even remotely connected with Jesus.

The owner of the inn tapped lightly on the door, came in noiselessly and lighted the oil lamp. It sent up a reluctant puff of smoke and flickered half-heartedly in the breeze from the open window.

"Are you hungry, Matthew?" I asked. "Shall we find supper for ourselves before the streets are completely dark?"

"Good!" he agreed enthusiastically. "The crowds around Jesus are always so great, the sick and the lame and the blind so constantly pleading, that I find it hard to remember when I last enjoyed a full meal."

It had grown quite dark by the time we returned to the inn, and there was a chill in the air from the winds which blew down from the snows on Mount Hermon. I suggested that we go into Matthew's room as it had had the benefit of the western sun.

After we had made ourselves comfortable, Matthew looked at me for a moment and spoke hesitantly. I sensed that he was about to say something to which he had given much thought.

"Claudius," he said, "in the last year you have become to me much like the son I should like to have. I have not failed to see your love for Mariamne and hers for you, and I am troubled many times wondering how it can terminate. Have you thought of the complications which will arise when you are ready to ask her to marry you?"

"I am ready, sir, and I have wished many times I had the courage to speak to you about it. I think of it when I am awake at night. I think of it in the early dawn. I think of it as I ride along the dusty roads. I picture myself going to Nicodemus and telling him that I, a Gentile, a superior officer in the Roman army, wish to ask for his daughter in marriage.

"I think of how it would be if I should tell my own parents that I wish to bring home a Jewish girl for my bride. I know that to them it would be almost as if I wished to bring a slave girl from Ethiopia or one of the concubines from the Arab kingdom, and I am sure that to Nicodemus and his wife—as far as their daughter is concerned—I stand in some such category."

Matthew sat silent for a long time, and I was fearful that I had offended him.

"The aristocratic Jews are a proud people, my son," he said, "as are those of the aristocracy in your own land. They do not wish to have their children mix with foreign blood. In Galilee where the people live simpler lives, I have known mixed marriages which have been happy and have caused small comment. But with a man of high position like Nicodemus, he and his family would become almost like outcasts among their social, political, and religious friends."

"I wonder why I could not have fallen in love with Susanna," I said, laughing.

Matthew did not laugh. There was pain in his eyes. "I wonder too," he said quietly, looking away.

I spoke hurriedly, not wanting the thoughts which seemed to hang heavy in the air to enter my mind.

"Matthew," I said, "I have wondered many times since that night I spent in the palace of Herod in Tiberias if the disciples of John the Baptist had tried to make of him something more than human, if they had tried to identify him with the great deliverer for whom your people have been waiting. You know quite well that there is nothing which can more readily create a hero or a martyr than a tragic death."

"Not in Palestine, Claudius," Matthew said positively. "If a tragic death, even one so cruel and monstrous as that of John, were all that is needed to create a god or a saint, there would be one on every street corner. Palestine is used to tragedy. When Antiochus Epiphanes ruled our land and endeavored to wipe out our religion, devout and patriotic Jews were crucified by the hundreds. But crucifixion cannot make a god. Crucifixions and violent deaths are too common here, I am ashamed to say, to make a Messiah of any man."

"Tell me what has happened since that day, Matthew, when I sailed back to Capernaum and found you and Jesus and the others gone."

That was the day, he told me, after he and the other men had returned from their first journey without Jesus. He had sent them out to teach some of the things he had taught them. They were not teachers. They were fishermen and farmers and businessmen, and they made many mistakes. Jesus knew how they had tried, how exhausted they were. He himself was very sad, and they set sail for a green plain just south of Bethsaida-Julias. The men knew the place well. There would be quiet there, and rest. They could stretch out on the soft grass and sleep.

When they reached the plain, they could not see the lush grass.

There were people—multitudes of them. People from Capernaum and the towns around the lake. To the disciples, a nameless, irksome mob of people who would rob them of their sleep. To Jesus they were sheep without a shepherd. He told them so when they begged him to send the crowds away. He told them of the kind of kingdom he had come to establish—a kingdom based on the love of God and upon the human response to this love involving kindness, understanding, and compassion for all men.

"I wonder why Jesus does not give us up!" Matthew said. "He might have chosen important men to follow him. We are nobodies! I am the only one who can keep us from being in actual want. Joanna, wife of Herod's steward Chuza, sends us money whenever old Chuza will give it to her. Peter, Andrew, and the Zebedees supply us with fish. Nathanael has a small farm from which he brings fresh and dried figs and occasionally a few root vegetables. We eat from our hands as we walk. The women keep us supplied with clothes as well as they can, but I dread the winter. We will all be cold.

"We bring Jesus nothing, Claudius. We do not understand him. Yesterday, here in Caesarea Philippi, he said a strange thing. He asked who men say that he is, and after we had told him, he said to us, 'Who do you say that I am?' Of course it was Peter who answered, 'We have believed, and have come to know, that you are the Holy One of God.' We all joined him. For a little while, Jesus' face seemed as if it were brighter than the sun, and then it grew sad. He told us he must go to Jerusalem in spite of the edict against him. He must be arrested, he said. He must suffer, and he must be put to death. He said something about rising again. We could not bear to listen. We argued with him. I do not know why he does not give us up!"

I looked at Matthew. On his face was a look of love and adoration. Matthew—dreading the long, cold winter, hating the stale bread and the raw vegetables—yet never thinking of turning back. I remembered the day I met him in the outdoor eating place in Capernaum, how I recognized the excellent cut of his robe and the fine material as indicative of a man of wealth. I thought of Matthew's fine estate. I thought of the banquet table, the food upon it. I thought of all the things Matthew had been willing, even eager, to relinquish in order to follow Jesus. I thought I knew why Jesus did not give them up.

Matthew continued his story of the day on the plain below Bethsaida-Julias.

It was almost dark, he said, when they awoke, and they went to Jesus—still teaching the people—and begged him to send them away so that they could buy themselves something to eat. They supposed Jesus spoke in jest when he asked how much food they themselves had. Andrew smiled and said that Philip's young cousin Caleb who was visiting in Capernaum, was carrying a little lunch. He had five hard rolls and two little fishes. We all laughed, and Andrew asked, "What is that among so many?"

Jesus did not laugh. "Bring them to me," he said.

He stood holding the grimy bundle in his hands. With his eyes he searched the crowd for the little boy. The smile he gave was something Caleb would never forget. It was as if he and Jesus had become partners.

The disciples were deeply concerned, Matthew said. They feared that Jesus was over-tired. When he told the people to sit down upon the ground, and began to open the lunch, they thought the people would laugh. They did not laugh.

They waited—expectantly—and when Jesus began to pray, they bowed their heads, and there was not a sound except a turtle dove calling mournfully from the treetops. After he had prayed, Jesus began to break the rolls and fishes. There seemed no end to the breaking. He gave the food to the disciples and they passed it among the throng. They ate. There were twelve basketfuls left over.

With my background of paganism, my familiarity with Greek philosophy, I had almost been able to persuade myself, since I had been away from Jesus, that the miracles I had seen him perform had in them elements of human response. People often could be swayed by a stronger will, I told myself, or by sheer magnetism of personality.

But cold fish from a little boy's grimy pocket! I sat still for a long moment, and then I asked, "How many people were there, Matthew?"

"Five thousand, not counting the women and children."

"Five thousand!"

"Yes, and the people wanted to take Jesus by force and make him a king. We were excited. We thought the time had come. But Jesus spoke to us quietly, telling us to get into the boat and sail toward Capernaum. We did not want to go. We wanted to stay and see what happened, and then we could see that nothing was going to happen.

"As we began to move toward the boat, we saw that Jesus was losing himself in the milling, hysterical throng, that he was looking wistfully to the trees on a nearby hillside, and we knew from experience that he would hide away there to pray."

"But why, Matthew?" I asked, embarrassed at the huskiness of my voice. "Why wouldn't he let them make him a king? This was one of those tense moments which occur only occasionally in history when one man can do what he wants with a crowd! If Jesus had gathered those five thousand men and all those women and children around him and had started marching toward Jerusalem, without doubt thousands more would have joined them on the way. The whole course of history might have been changed— and for good!"

Matthew agreed. He said the disciples had felt that Jesus was missing his greatest opportunity.

"This occurs to me also, Matthew," I told him, still excited, "if Jesus could transform Caleb's little lunch into food for so many, why does he let you and Thomas and the others keep struggling with figs, and fish, and vegetables, dreading the cold of the winter? Why does he not replenish your supply of food and clothing when there is need?"

Matthew smiled, picked up a glass of water, and drank it.

"Nothing has ever come nearer to tearing our little group apart than that question," he said. "We were excited with the idea you have suggested, and as we sailed toward our homes, the men who had always been poor began to plan what they could buy for their families. The Zebedees began to argue about who was going to be the highest in the fabulous kingdom Jesus was sure to establish. When Peter's temper began to rise, and he said John and James had no more right than the rest of us to a high position, the boys answered that they would ask their mother to go with them to

Jesus and persuade him to confer on them the highest places—
one on his right hand and one on his left.

"Judas began to figure the profit we could make if Jesus took a
small amount of food each morning and changed it into enough
to feed thousands, and we could sell it in the open market.

"We were all very disagreeable to each other about it. We are
glad that Jesus does not know. Philip reminded us that Jesus never
thought highly of miracles for themselves alone, that he performed
them only when there was some actual need, and never to keep a
person from doing something he could do for himself. He reminded us that we once had heard Jesus say to a group who questioned him, "If you can believe for no other reason, then believe
for the very works' sake."

"It is hard for me to understand, Matthew."

"And for us. We have decided, however, that Jesus would not
let them make him king because of their motive. That you must
agree, Claudius, was no higher than their well-filled stomachs.
They wanted him to be their king because of the free bread and
meat. They wanted to enthrone him so they might live without
effort or striving.

"That is not what Jesus wants. Not once has he promised it.
Not once has he promised us a constantly smooth lake with no
storms or struggles with the sails. He promises only that when the
waves dash, and the wind is against us, he will help us weather
the storm."

As I lay on my couch after Matthew was asleep, I thought of
Susanna and of how she had said the same sort of words to me
one day in Capernaum. Dear Susanna, I thought. I smiled in the
darkness when I thought of little Caleb. I was glad it was his lunch
Jesus used. I thought of the forthrightness with which Matthew
had told me of the quarrel on the boat.

I thought most of Mariamne.

Return to Jerusalem

Matthew left Caesarea Philippi, and I found the resort town swiftly losing its appeal. I wanted to start back to Jerusalem. I wanted to see Mariamne.

My business for Pilate in determining the advisability of consolidating the smaller Roman forts was ended, and since I needed only to revisit the tax-collectors whom I had investigated on my way toward Galilee, I decided I should begin my journey southward as soon as possible. Travel was slow at best, and with the numerous stops I would make on the way, several months would pass before I could reach Jerusalem.

I found few changes in the publicans. Easy money is not relinquished hastily unless a man has great strength of character or a powerful incentive outside himself.

As the months went by, and I passed through Decapolis and through the northern part of Peraea, as I came nearer to the place where I was to cross the Jordan River into the province of Judea, I began to dread the day when I would reach the town of Jericho where the publican Zacchaeus lived. For some of the tax-collectors I might have entertained a faint hope that their ways might be mended, but not Zacchaeus. I remembered with what cynicism and actual cruelty he had spoken to me of the man from the slums whose wife lay ill and whose children cried for food. His lips were tight-drawn as he told me, "You cannot help them. Once you start they are forever on your back."

One thing seemed sure to me. I would go to Jericho armed with excuses so that I need spend no time in Zacchaeus' house. His ivory gods and goddesses on their carven shelf would never again bring me a feeling of sickness as if I had reached out my hand and touched a venomous serpent.

In Peraea, as in Decapolis, the talk was of Jesus. He was the subject of continual controversy. Some believed that Jesus of Nazareth was indeed the Son of God. To many he was only a good man, a great teacher, a healer of the sick and lame and blind. To others he was one who perverted the people. They feared he would start a riot and bring the cruel Roman soldiers down about their heads.

Many people feared for him. They feared the southward journey which he had steadfastly set before him. They knew about the edict. They knew the power of the members of the Sanhedrin, the Pharisees, the scribes, the priests. They knew, and they were afraid. They would ask if I had seen him as I traveled. They were disappointed that our paths had not crossed, and they wanted to tell me many times of his miracles, his teachings, his strange determination to reach Jerusalem.

The small town across the river from Jericho was agog with talk when I arrived there to spend the night. People, old and young, gathered about to tell the story of Jesus' visit on the Sabbath day just gone by. I was the only stranger, and it was good to have the story fall on fresh ears.

A Pharisee, a ruler in the synagogue, had given a supper. It was for the elect, but desiring to entrap Jesus and thus enlarge his standing before the chief priests in the Temple in Jerusalem—perhaps securing for himself a more lucrative place among the Temple dignitaries—he had invited Jesus to attend and with him, a great, lumbering man of the township who was the butt of jibes and jeers from the populace. An abnormal accumulation of fluid in the man's body made him swollen and grotesque.

Jesus, entering the room, looked upon the man, who sat cowering and miserable—miserable that attention should be centered upon him, miserable that he should be there at all. Jesus put his hand upon the man. He healed him, and led him to the door. He let him go.

Turning back, he spoke. He asked them a question. "Which of you, having an ass or an ox that has fallen into a well, will not immediately pull him out on a Sabbath day?"

They were taken aback. Their plans were going awry. It was

they who had purposed to ask the questions. They did not answer; they did not know the shape their words should take.

Jesus was not finished with them. He looked from one end of the laden table to the other. It was as if he spoke to each man and to him alone.

"I watched you as you came in, each one seeking the best seat for himself. When you are invited to a feast, there may be those of greater honor than yourself in attendance. It may be that when you are seated, the host will come and put his hand upon your shoulder and ask you to move to a lower place. When you are invited, seek the lowest seat, so that the one who has invited you will come and say, 'Friend, go up higher.' Then you will be honored in the presence of all who sit with you. Everyone who exalts himself will be humbled, and he who humbles himself will be exalted."

Speaking to the host, he had said, "When you give a feast, do not invite only those who can repay, but invite the poor, the maimed, the lame, and the blind."

The host did not like it, nor did the guests. Their purpose was not accomplished. Jesus should be forced into a position which would necessitate his justifying his behavior because he had healed on the Sabbath. They had planned it well; yet they were overwhelmed with a need to justify their own grasping selfishness, their eagerness to hold the places of preeminence. They were chagrined, and they began to whisper behind their hands, to whisper and to laugh.

Outside the door, the common people had gathered. When he got outside, Jesus began to talk to them. He told them that it was not a cheap nor an easy thing to be a follower of his. It cost something, he said, and many started to walk away. They felt no desire for that which involved hardship or added responsibilities. Their lives were hard enough already. But when the stories began, they came back.

A man had one hundred sheep, Jesus told them, and when one strayed away, he left the ninety-nine to search for the one that was lost. He carried it home in his arms. Many who listened were shepherds. They knew about sheep.

A woman had ten coins, he said, and lost one. She lighted a

candle, seized her broom, and swept under every piece of furniture until she found it, and then she called to her neighbors, "Rejoice! I have found the coin which I had lost!" They laughed, but not in derision as the Pharisees had laughed.

"There was a boy," Jesus had said, "rebellious of authority. Rebellious, he took all of his inheritance into a far country and squandered it in loose living." Even as the people told me, I knew the ending. I had heard it one night in Bethany from a real boy, rebellious and frustrated.

"Even so, I tell you, there is joy before the angels of God over one sinner who repents," Jesus said.

Jesus' visit had meant something to the people in the little town. Because of it, the things he had done, the things he had said, each man and each woman felt a new worth. Perhaps, I thought, they held their heads a little higher, realizing their importance to their God.

+   +   +

When I came to Jericho I saw the same beautiful palm trees lining the streets, the roses blooming in profusion in the parkways. I could see the great old palace in its prominent place, the hippodrome, the citadel on the hill. But somehow, as on that early morning when I had left the house of Zacchaeus on my way toward Decapolis, I found myself looking, not at these things of beauty, or at the pretentious residential district, but over toward the east, where the Jordan River flowed, and where the poor, the downtrodden, the despised, and the underprivileged lived.

As soon as I was well into the city, I was able to discern that something unusual was in progress. I knew it was near the time for the Passover festival, but I could not understand why this should have drawn the excited, pushing, babbling crowds into the streets of Jericho since the celebration of the Jewish feasts took place in Jerusalem. Soon I was able to catch the words which were being shouted from one to another as they hurried along.

"He is over in the part of town where the rich live!" some were saying, "near the house of the publican, Zacchaeus!" "Zacchaeus will have him driven away," others answered. "Zacchaeus will

have him taxed for walking on his street," someone shouted, and
the crowd roared with laughter. It was laughter filled with
bitterness.

I felt fortunate to be going in the direction of the throng. Because so many people were now in the streets which led to the
section where the mansion of Zacchaeus stood, it would have
been difficult to turn aside or go by any other way. As I walked
and was pushed along, I felt in wholehearted agreement with the
shouting of the crowd. I too felt certain that the haughty and
self-centered Zacchaeus would never permit this parade to pass
unchallenged on his exclusive street. I could picture him peeking
out from behind the heavy, lustrous draperies and giving indig-
nant orders to his servants to have the street cleared immediately.

Suddenly I heard the tenor of the shouting change. They were
no longer speaking of the temerity of Jesus to walk upon Zacchaeus' street. Now there was sincere amazement and disbelief in
their voices.

"It is!" they were shouting. "It cannot be!" other voices mingled.
"He would never come out among unimportant people! Zacchaeus
never would be so undignified as to climb a tree! It must be somebody who looks like him! Let me by! Let me by! Let me see!"

On the very edge of Zacchaeus' property, with its branches
reaching out over the street, was a gnarled sycamore tree. I felt
the same amazement and disbelief as they when I raised my eyes
above the crowd and saw the repulsive little tax-collector of
Jericho sitting rather precariously in the branches.

I am not at all sure that I did not feel some inner desire to
humiliate him when I called out his name in a loud voice. I am
certain it was not that I felt any yearning to renew our acquaintance.

"Zacchaeus!" I called, and I could see at once that he had hoped
the wide green leaves would protect him from the sight of those
on the ground. When he recognized me, his face looked ready to
burst with its rush of dark red blood.

"Merely curious concerning the peasant preacher about whom
we hear so much," he stuttered. "Merely curious! Very unpleasant
mob of nobodies! I shall have them driven away immediately.
You should have let me know you were coming, Tribune. Come

into my house. You must have supper at my table. Very unpleasant affair!"

While Zacchaeus still was sputtering away, the crowd suddenly lost all interest in him. "Jesus!" the cry went up. "Jesus is passing this way!"

Every eye turned upon the young man who was now coming down Zacchaeus' street, and immediately I remembered the words I had heard Philip use about him, and the thoughts I myself had had when I had seen him walking down the street in front of Matthew's customs office in Capernaum. Again he seemed to be walking with a complete joy in life and all that surrounded him.

Some of those nearest him began to shout to the others, "His power has not run out! He just gave a blind man his sight! We saw him do it! We tried to drive the beggar away, but Jesus stopped him and healed him, and the man went running to his house laughing and crying and praising God! You never saw such a sight!"

I glanced up into the sycamore tree. Zacchaeus was still there, and he was looking down into Jesus' face as if he were spell-bound. Jesus was looking straight into the eyes of Zacchaeus.

"Come down, Zacchaeus," he said quietly. "I wish to have supper at your house."

I wished he had not asked. I knew Zacchaeus would answer in his snobbish, hateful manner. I knew without doubt that he would never let Jesus come into his house.

Many times in Galilee I had seen men and women change in the presence of Jesus. I had seen the sick made well, the lame get up and walk, the blind rubbing their eyes in wonderment as they looked out upon a world new to them, but I had never witnessed a more spectacular change in any of them than I saw now in Zacchaeus.

There was no embarrassment in his speech or manner. There was no snobbishness or hatred. He began to climb down out of the tree with a kind of dignity, if it is possible to climb out of a tree with dignity. But his answer was more surprising than his behavior.

"I will come down immediately, sir," he said, with the courtesy and respect I should have supposed he would have shown only to royalty. "I will have my servants wash your feet, and we will have supper as soon as they can prepare the best that is in my larder."

He glanced back at me. "Come in, Tribune," he said, with a kindness in his voice which I had never heard. "You will remember the room you had when you were here before. Make yourself comfortable. Supper will be served in an hour."

I walked into Zacchaeus' house behind him. He had motioned for Jesus to go in ahead and had signaled for me to follow. When we passed into the great entrance hall, he waved his hand for me to go up the stairs, and he walked with Jesus into that garish reception room, with its shelf of beautifully carved gods and goddesses of the Greeks and Romans, and he closed the door.

I had no trouble in finding the room I had occupied on my strange and disagreeable visit two years earlier. I put my luggage down, and had just stretched out on the couch to wait for the imposing servant to come and announce that supper would be served in the gold room, when I heard a clamor on the outside even greater than the one I had heard earlier in the evening. I went to the front window, and I could see that the crowd was still milling about but that something had renewed their interest, so that they were shouting and pointing and trying to push past each other to get to a more advantageous position.

I hastened down the stairs to see what was happening, and as I went out the door, I could see Jesus and Zacchaeus standing together. Jesus was holding up his hand for quiet, and the throng obeyed him.

"Now, Zacchaeus!" he said, so softly that I could barely hear the words.

The repulsive, overbearing, greedy little man began to talk, and the words which came out of his mouth were so different, so contrary to any words I had ever heard him use, that I found myself rubbing my own eyes as I had seen the blind do when they had received their sight. I could not believe what I was seeing. I could not believe what I was hearing.

Zacchaeus spoke, and the crowd stood silent and listened. Some mouths were wide open, and they seemed unable to close them again.

"Listen to me!" he said, not arrogantly, but with evident sincerity. "Listen to me! I am a rich man, and the half of all my possessions I am going to give to the poor of this town. From what is left, I want to repay all those of you and the other citizens of Jericho whom I have taxed unjustly. You go now to all the business houses which are still open. Go to the residences of the wealthy. Go to the slum district in the river bottoms. Tell everybody to make out their claims, and in whatever degree I have collected taxes above that which was legal, I will give to each man four times the amount!"

They began to disperse slowly, as if they were in a trance. Zacchaeus had another thought. "Wait!" he called to them. "Come back! You first must have something to eat. I know that you are tired and hungry. Come in, all of you!"

The people looked at each other in silent wonder. A few spoke softly—as if they were in a temple.

It was only about seventeen miles from Jericho to Jerusalem, and as I traveled those miles, I thought about Zacchaeus. I would never have believed there could be such a change in a man. I remembered that my reaction to him on my first visit to Jericho had been one of actual loathing. He had seemed to personify everything that was cold, cruel, and malignant, as he had made his plans to exact more and more taxes from the poor people, waking up in the night and amusing himself by compiling new lists of the preposterous things upon which he might place a tax.

Yesterday, his whole countenance seemed to have changed. There were no longer the tight, drawn lips, the calculating squint of the eyes, and his manner had become almost lacking in self-satisfaction. He even looked as if he might have gained an inch or two in height.

I asked myself what could have brought it about, and I knew the answer. He had come close to Jesus. He loved Jesus and wanted to be well-pleasing to him.

Suppose, I thought to myself as I rode along, that Jesus could be the one his followers believe him to be. Suppose every person who learns to love him, and to know him, as Zacchaeus has done, should be changed as Zacchaeus has been changed. What kind of world would result? Would this be the kingdom about which I have heard so much from Matthew, Mariamne, and Susanna?

Would the whole world have peace and good will toward one another? Would there be no more wars, no more fighting, no more effort to perfect deadlier weapons to wipe each other from the face of the earth? Would people feel toward each other only kindness and consideration, each one preferring the other to himself? Would each choose the lowest seat for himself instead of the highest, as Jesus had said that he should? Would people sometimes invite those who never could repay them?

I had to admit that I did not believe it could be possible. I thought about Lazarus and how he had said, "I do not know. I seem to be waiting." I wondered if Lazarus had found that for which he waited.

I, too, seemed to be waiting.

It was early on Friday afternoon when I rode into Jerusalem. It was almost exactly like the early afternoon when I had arrived there for the first time. Again the Passover crowds were filling the streets, pushing against each other, trying to get into the Temple, into the shops, into the inns.

It was almost the same, but there was a difference. It was in the prevailing atmosphere. On the day I arrived, there had been a gay holiday mood everywhere. A few of the visitors had seemed serious and intent upon worship, but for the most part it was more like some great festival in the cities of Athens or Rome. Today this was not true. Today the crowds were even greater, so that one could barely move through the main streets, and the alleyways were equally congested.

The difference which impressed me most, however, was the expression on the faces of the people. On many there was a definite look of fear, of deep concern, and on others a kind of repressed excitement as if they were waiting for something to happen. Not actually hoping for tragedy, but ready if it should occur, to experience whatever thrill it might bring.

Everywhere now the conversation seemed to be much the same —in the street, in the alleys, on the corners, wherever people could make themselves heard. "Do you think he will not come to the feast?" they were asking each other.

I went to the tower immediately. I wished to report my presence in Jerusalem and to determine if there were instructions from Pilate as to when I was to present my report to him. I felt a real joy in seeing my friend Zoldi again. We took one look at each other and laughed, much as we had done when we first met.

"No need for me to wonder about the state of my health after my extended journey," I said. "I can see without a mirror that I am looking quite well! But Zoldi," I continued, now in a serious mood, "as I came through the streets, I felt an evident sense of fear and excitement. It was exactly as if all those multitudes were waiting for something to happen, some of them dreading it, some waiting as one might wait for a chariot to overturn in a race so that there would be an additional thrill to the events of the day."

"They are waiting, Lysias," Zoldi agreed. "They wait with the very emotions which you have expressed. I too, the other tribunes, the centurions, the common soldiers, we all wait, but for a different reason. We do not know what will happen, but of one thing we are convinced. If Jesus comes into Jerusalem while the Passover is in progress, there is going to be trouble.

"There is an edict against his coming here. Any person discovering his whereabouts must report it to the Sanhedrin or find himself in dire straits. Any person daring to express belief in him will be excommunicated. It is whispered that many of the rulers believe in him now but know what it would cost them if they should let it be known.

"The whole city is tense. Never in all the years I have been here have I witnessed such tenseness. If Jesus comes—and there are those who say he will come, that for the last six months he has set his face steadfastly toward this city—if he comes, I tell you, Lysias, there will be rioting. If the rulers arrest him while these crowds are here, we will have blood running in the streets."

"Will the people who believe in him fight?"

"I am told he will not allow them to fight, that he has said he could call a legion of angels if he has need of help, and that the kingdom he has come to establish is not to be founded on the blood of battle, but of sacrifice. The rulers have ordered his arrest, however, and how well Jesus could control the tremendous crowds who love him and believe in him as the Son of God, I do not know. One thing is to our advantage. The rulers have stipulated that the arrest not be on the feast day in order to avoid having a tumult among the people."

"When is the feast day?" I asked.

"One week from today—next Friday."

A messenger from Nicodemus asking me to come to his house for the evening meal interrupted us.

I could hardly wait. As I had approached nearer and nearer to Jerusalem, I had thought constantly of Mariamne. I felt that I knew what was in her heart as she knew what was in mine. As I dressed, I wondered if I should discuss with her the wide difference in our backgrounds, the certain opposition of her parents and mine. I wondered if I should ask if we dared to hope and plan together, or whether we should let the beauty and sweetness of our present relationship continue without facing problems which seemed to have no solution.

When the servant opened the door to Nicodemus' house, Mariamne was standing in the entrance hall, as she had been waiting that day at Matthew's. Today no words were spoken. Her eyes were shining; in the passing moment, I thought how beautiful she was; and she was in my arms.

There was no need for planning what I ought to do.

For many hours after Mariamne and her mother had gone up the stairs for the night, Nicodemus and I sat talking. I sensed the same tenseness in him which I had felt in the people of the streets. He wanted to talk about Jesus.

"I have wondered often how you have come to feel about him, Lysias," he said. "In deepest confidence I want to tell you that, like Joshua of old, I must declare my belief. As for me and my house, we will serve Jesus as Lord. I say 'serve,' Lysias, but I do not actually mean it. I mean only that we believe. We believe that he is the Christ, the Son of God. But we do not serve him. We do not call his name. We do not dare."

Nicodemus left his chair. He poured a glass of wine, lifted it to his lips, and set it down upon the table. The lines in his face dug in as if they had been etched with sharp nails.

"You think I am a coward, Lysias. You are right—I am. I believe, but I cannot give up the things for which I have spent my life. I cannot give up my position in the Supreme Court. I cannot relinquish my place as an honored and accredited educator in Palestine. I cannot bear to see my wife and daughter become outcasts from the social positions they hold in Jerusalem and in Rome. I cannot bear to think of excommunication for all of us from the Temple where we have worshiped so long."

As Nicodemus talked, my hopes for any happiness with Mariamne seemed foolish and fleeting.

"Are you sure, sir," I asked, "that your friends would behave as you fear?"

"I am sure. Let me tell you of something which happened as long ago as last July when Jesus came down to Jerusalem to attend the Feast of the Tabernacles. He came secretly because already the rulers sought to kill him."

"Tell me, sir," I said, preoccupied and sad, thinking I need not listen.

I listened, however, stopping him only occasionally to ask a question, and more often leaning forward in my chair in my eagerness not to miss a word.

The Feast of the Tabernacles, he told me, was one of the three great annual feasts, not as great as the Passover, but of high importance. Originally it had lasted for seven days, but an eighth day had been added, a day of great significance.

On the first seven days, a procession of priests carrying silver vessels filled with water, marched into the Temple and poured the water out before the congregation, symbolizing the water which God had given to the Jewish people in the wilderness, and reminding them of the great deliverer he was to send.

On the eighth day there was no procession, no silver vessels, no water. This symbolized that the promised Messiah had not yet come.

It had been on this important eighth day that Jesus had stood in the Temple, and cried in a loud voice to all who were assembled there, "If any one thirst, let him come to me and drink."

The people seemed frozen in their amazement. He—Jesus of Nazareth, a carpenter, an itinerant preacher from Galilee—was standing in their sacred Temple on this most sacred day of the feast and proclaiming publicly that it was he who could supply all their needs. "He who believes in me . . ." Jesus continued, "out of his heart shall flow rivers of living water!"

Over in the Council Chamber, Nicodemus said, a hastily assembled meeting of the Sanhedrin was taking place. It had been reported to the High Priest that Jesus was teaching openly in the Temple. Already he knew that Jerusalem was filled with talk concerning him. Now he was told people were asking each other, "Is not this the man whom they seek to kill? Here he is, speaking openly, and they say nothing to him!" Some were whispering, "Can it be that the authorities really know that this is the Christ?"

Hearing now of this latest indignity, the High Priest and the elders were frantic. They hurriedly dispatched a messenger up the stairs of the Tower demanding that officers go into the Temple, arrest Jesus, and bring him before them.

The officers, having heard nothing, but knowing the sudden uproars which could take place during a feast, impressed because the messenger insisted he had come at the command of the High Priest himself, and that he had demanded that officers, and not common soldiers, make the arrest, seized their swords and whatever they could of their full regalia, and went into the Temple.

There was complete quiet there, Nicodemus told me, except for the voice of Jesus. He said it was reported that the officers stood still—listening—that they behaved more like worshipers at a shrine than like arresting officers.

When Jesus had finished speaking, he walked past them. He walked out of the Temple door. The Roman officers did not say a word but started marching solemnly across the great paving stones of the Court of the Gentiles and into the Council Chamber.

"Well?" Caiaphas, the High Priest demanded, "where is he? Why did you not bring him?"

The officers made no excuse. "No man ever spoke like this man," they stated simply.

The High priest and the members of the Sanhedrin were filled with indignation. Their orders had been ignored. It was as if each one had been offered a personal affront.

"Have you also come to believe in him?" they asked with biting sarcasm.

Then, as if the question gave the final answer, the conclusive evidence, to all further uncertainty concerning Jesus, they added, "Have any of the authorities or of the Pharisees believed in him?"

They were saying in effect that if the important people, the rulers, had not believed, then certainly Jesus must be an imposter, not worthy of belief, but the officers made no answer. They marched stiffly across the stones and up the tower stairs.

Nicodemus left his chair and began to walk about the room. I could see that he was deeply moved.

"Lysias," he said, "I knew that the members of the Court suspected some of us. I knew that my friend Joseph of Arimathea headed the list and that I perhaps stood next. A sudden cold terror seized my heart. I was afraid. I was afraid for my wife, for Mariamne, and for myself. I was afraid for the twelve men who had followed Jesus so closely. I was afraid for all the thousands of unimportant people who love him and believe in him. I was afraid for Jesus. But I could not keep silent. The question came forth almost without my volition, almost as if someone else were speaking."

"What did you say, sir?" I asked eagerly.

"I said to them as coldly as if I were trying a case, 'Does our law judge a man without first giving him a hearing?'

"They turned their wrath upon me. 'Does the great Nicodemus also come from Galilee?'" they shouted.

Nicodemus returned to his chair. He spoke slowly and with sorrow in his voice.

"Claudius, my friend," he said, "I looked at that group of educated, aristocratic gentlemen. I saw the hatred and the fear in their faces. They did not want the Messiah to come! They did not want to give up their easy religion, their easy positions. I knew that nothing could deter them in their determination to hold on to those things.

"And yet, strangely enough, as I sat there in that Council Chamber, knowing their power, I was somehow certain that no mortal man, whether ruler in Israel or Roman officer, will ever be able to take Jesus until he is ready to be taken."

When I returned to the Tower late that night, I found a communication from Pilate saying he would be in Jerusalem all of the following week, and that he would expect me to make my report on the following Friday afternoon. I decided at once that I would spend the next day, which was Saturday, the Jewish Sabbath, out in Bethany with Martha and Mary and Lazarus. I knew that after Martha and Mary had returned from their walk across the Mount of Olives into Jerusalem to attend the services in the Temple, there would be no more work for the day.

I arrived late in the morning, and if our acquaintance had been one of many years, I could not have been made more welcome by the three of them. I felt the same warmth and friendliness which I had experienced when I had gone so hesitantly to their home as my first stop on the journey from which I had just returned.

Everything seemed much the same, and yet there was something in the air—something pulsating, vibrant!

It was a little like the excitement one feels just before the curtain is raised on a thrilling drama. I could not identify it, but I knew it was there. Martha still seemed busy about many things, but while, on my first visit, she had given the impression of being impelled by some inner urgency as if she must finish one task so that she might get to another, she moved now without haste and with quiet efficiency. Mary was still the same, still with that attractive look of a freshly-scrubbed little girl. But Mary was excited. Her eyes were bright, and she would place her palms together, and rub them—fast and hard. Once I saw Martha look at her and shake her head.

There was no mistaking the change in Lazarus. He was a transformed person. He had changed from a boy to a man. There was nothing about him now of the adolescent, no sense of rebellion, no look of frustration, no evidence of indecision as to what he wished to do with his life. He was secure, steadfast, to be depended upon.

When we sat down to eat, it was as if we waited for something. The red soup was hot and delicious. There was even a small dish of roasted calf which they told me had been brought in by a neighbor. There were the cakes hot from the hearth, and the butter to spread upon them, and the wild honey. When Martha brought in the dessert, she smiled proudly. She had remembered how much I enjoyed her date pudding, and had prepared her most delectable recipe. But I knew we were waiting for something. Mary and Lazarus would glance at each other, their eyes alive with some thrilling secret, and Mary was rubbing her palms again.

Suddenly she burst out, "I cannot wait one more minute! Let Lazarus tell him now, Martha!"

Martha looked at her indulgently and smiled. "When we saw you coming, Tribune, I made them promise to wait until we finished our meal. It is not good to swallow too much excitement with one's food."

"Happiness could hurt no one," Mary insisted.

Martha leaned back on her cushioned bench. "Tell him, my brother. It is your story. We will not interrupt."

Lazarus got up, and stood behind Martha's bench. He put his hand lovingly on her shoulder. "You tell your part of it, Marty," he said, "just do not let Mary tell it all as she usually does."

"I do not!" said Mary.

"Tribune," Martha said, "Lazarus has not called me 'Marty' since he was a little boy and used to come to me to have his hurts kissed and made well."

"And now I call her that all the time."

It was as if they were deliberately holding back. It was as if they made small conversation to delay the telling of their story, as if they could not bear to begin the telling because they could not bear to have something so wonderful come to an end.

It was Lazarus who started. "I have been dead!"

"You have been dead, Lazarus!"

"Look at me, Tribune Lysias! Touch me! Feel the strength of my muscles! I am a man who has been dead four days, and who has been raised to health and strength again."

Lazarus came to stand in front of me. He held out his great, strong arm. He doubled his other fist, and beat vigorously on his broad chest.

"Tell me, Lazarus," I said, the excitement beginning to beat in my throat also.

He talked, walking about the room, stopping to pat Martha's shoulder, to give Mary's head a small push.

"It was like this, Tribune," he said. "Jesus had been here for the night, and in the early morning after he started on his way, I went out to help Martha with the weeding. Suddenly, I was faint and sick. I loosened my tunic at the throat because I was hot, and yet the cold perspiration poured from my forehead. My head ached, and things were spinning around in a kind of gray darkness sprinkled with dancing, shining dots. When I found myself in my bed, with Martha and Mary and the neighbors standing around, I did not know how I had come there. I held on to Marty's hand like a frightened child."

Martha joined in. "Lazarus had never been ill before," she said. "We know little about illness, but immediately we sent a messenger across the Jordan to find Jesus."

"I knew Jesus would heal me," said Lazarus. "I had seen him heal people who were old, or who had no strong body like mine. I knew he would heal me.

"We waited. We waited one day—and another—and another—and another. Each day I grew worse, and I was afraid. I have never been so afraid, Tribune! I did not want to die. I thought of all the things I had wanted to do, all the places I had wanted to go. I wished I had been nicer to Marty and had helped her more. There were even times when I wished I had not fought with Mary."

Lazarus smiled. "Mary never doubted that Jesus would come," he said, and hesitated for a moment.

"Tell Tribune Lysias the truth, my brother," Martha said. "Tell

him that your sister Martha doubted Jesus. I was overwhelmed
with bitterness, sir. I complained to everyone I saw. Over and
over I would say, 'He has pretended to be our friend. He has eaten
our food. He has stayed in our house, and now when we need
him he will not come!'"

"The day came," Lazarus continued, "when Martha and Mary
and Jesus and God and the street merchants in Jerusalem were all
confused in my mind. I worried because once I had said that I did
not know if there was a God. But I remembered the story Jesus
had told me about the boy who was dirty from feeding the hogs,
and how his father ran to meet him when he came home.

"I hoped God would come running to meet me, but I did not
want to die. Sometimes I thought I really was the boy who had
run away from home, and the hogs were all over my bed. They
nibbled at my hands and my feet, and I could not drive them
away. When I opened my eyes to tell Marty to help me, my eye-
balls hurt, and the faces of my sisters and the neighbors all ran
together."

The tears were streaming down Martha's face, but she took up
the story. "He died, Tribune Lysias!" she said. "He died, and we
wrapped him in the winding sheet, and put the spices around
him, and the napkin of linen around his head. We laid him in
the tomb.

"You have never seen anyone more bitter than I! My brother
was dead, and Jesus had turned away from us in our time of
need. Mary sat in the house, as one is supposed to do in time of
sorrow, but I had no consideration for the conventionalities of
religion. For more than three days I walked the streets of
Bethany. I roamed the countryside.

"On the fourth day, runners came into the town shouting,
'Martha! Mary! Everybody! Jesus is coming!'

"When I saw him, I could not restrain my bitterness. My heart
softened for a moment when I saw his face, but not enough.
'Lord,' I cried, 'if you had been here, my brother would not have
died!'

"'Your brother will rise again,' Jesus said to me gently, but
this was no comfort to me. I wanted my brother, and I answered
him sullenly, 'I know that he will rise again in the resurrection

at the last day.' Jesus spoke slowly, and softly, and very clearly.

" 'I am the resurrection and the life,' he said. 'He who believes in me, though he die, yet shall he live. And whoever lives and believes in me shall never die. Do you believe this, Martha?'

"Tribune Lysias, it was as if I had never seen Jesus before. 'Yes,' I answered him. 'I believe that you are the Christ, the Son of God!'

"Jesus sent me to get Mary, and all the people from the village began to gather. We led him to the tomb. He called out in a loud voice so that the great crowd could hear, 'Lazarus! Come out.'

"And he did, Tribune Lysias! Lazarus came out. He had a strange and eerie look with the winding sheet around his body and the napkin around his head, but he was not pale, he was not sick, there were no signs of death upon his body. I knew that the words were true which Jesus had spoken to me as we walked toward the tomb and I had begged him not to go near. 'Did I not tell you, Martha,' he had said, 'that if you would believe you would see the glory of God?' "

"We have seen the glory of God, sir," Mary said.

"We have seen the glory of God!" Lazarus repeated.

+ + +

I slept late the next morning. It was Sunday, and since Pilate did not wish to receive my report until the following Friday, I had decided I would have a few days of relaxation, but suddenly I was awakened by the sound of shouting.

I hurried to the window, and I could hear people calling excitedly, "Hurry! Hurry! Jesus is coming into the city! He is defying the rulers! He is riding in on the back of an ass! He is coming around the bend of the road on the Mount of Olives!"

I wondered if he had spent the night with Martha and Mary and Lazarus in Bethany. I shook my head. I could not understand why he had come into the city when he knew the edict, when he knew the danger. The streets were so crowded with visitors that he might well have entered furtively and have lost himself in the throngs, but this was the most spectacular way he could have chosen.

I had learned much of Jewish prophecy on my journey and had written parts of it into the article I was preparing. I knew this prophecy, as did all those screaming, shouting, excited Jews. "Lo, your king comes to you; triumphant and victorious is he, humble and riding on an ass, on a colt, the foal of an ass."

I thought of what Matthew had told me of the time the crowds outside Bethsaida-Julias had tried to crown Jesus king after he had fed the multitudes. He had not been ready then. I wondered if he was ready now.

I dressed hurriedly and made my way to the stairs. Zoldi joined me on the top step. "This is what we have been dreading," he said. "These Jews know their prophecies, and it is possible that they may try to crown Jesus king before this day is ended. If they do, there will be trouble indeed.

"At least one hundred thousand people must be milling around in these streets, and a riot could start without a moment's notice. I have stationed those tribunes who are in the city, the centurions and their men who are available, in strategic places, but this open approach is something upon which we had not counted."

"Zoldi," I told him, "my friend Matthew has told me that once he saw a crowd, not as large as this one, but equally excited, try to take Jesus by force and make him king. He controlled that crowd, and I think he can control this one. Unless he wishes to be crowned king, I think all their plans and their hysteria will come to nothing."

Zoldi looked at me strangely. "Have you come to believe in him, Lysias?" he asked.

"I do not know," I answered. "I seem to be waiting for something. Perhaps today, if he should let them make him king, it is that for which I wait. One thing I believe. If this is the day he wishes to establish the kingdom which his followers say he has come to establish, he can do it. And neither you, I, the rulers who hate him, nor the entire Roman army can do one thing to stop him."

"I think you do believe in him, Lysias."

"I repeat that I do not know. Some deep yearning in my heart seems quiet when I see him or hear his voice, but I have heard of strange claims which he has made for himself which convince me that there can be no half-way ground in one's belief in him. A man cannot make such claims unless he is indeed divine, as Matthew and the others believe him to be, or unless he is an imposter.

"Of this I am sure. When I am finally convinced, I will either believe with all my heart that Jesus is the Christ, the Son of God, or I will know that he is completely untrustworthy."

We had come now to the madly shouting procession as it came into the city. People waving palm branches which they had torn from the trees as they passed by. People running in front of the little colt, taking off their outer garments, laying them on the ground for Jesus to ride upon. The multitudes were shouting and singing, "Hosanna! Hosanna to the Son of David! Blessed be he who comes in the name of the Lord!"

The excitement that permeated the air made it hard to breathe normally—it made one's throat catch, as if in a sudden, unexpected sob.

I looked into the faces of the throng as they passed by. I could tell they thought this was the event for which they had been waiting. Marching just in front of Jesus, waving their palm branches, shouting and singing with the rest, were the men whom I had come to know back in Galilee.

I saw the rugged Peter, his head thrown back, singing louder than anybody. I saw the Zebedees, John and James, each with a hand on the little colt—as if assured that now they were about to take the positions which they coveted, one on Jesus' right hand and one on his left. Philip was there, as were Thomas and Judas.

I recalled what Matthew had told me of Judas totalling the amount of profit they could make if Jesus would perform a miracle each morning, turning a few fishes and stale rolls into quantities of food which they could sell to the populace in the market place. I wondered now if he was computing the revenue which could be collected from the worshiping multitude if Jesus should be crowned king.

I saw Matthew, but Matthew waved no branches. There was no song on his lips. He was looking at Jesus with deep adoration in his eyes, but his face portrayed sorrow and great fear. I felt sure that Matthew did not think Jesus was going to make himself a king.

I found myself joining in with the expectation of the crowd, wondering how Jesus would bring about his coronation. Would there be a sudden, decisive battle, now that these thousands were with him? Would they be able to overcome the Jerusalem garrison since we were not prepared for an attack? Would Jesus perform some miracle which would reduce us all to complete helplessness, and then proclaim his right to rule the world?

I pushed as near to him as I could. The procession had come to a halt, and Jesus was speaking. I leaned forward to be sure I would not miss his words. I wanted to hear how he would announce his rule, what manifesto he would proclaim. I heard, but the words were not the ones I had anticipated. They were not words of power, but of infinite sadness.

"Oh, Jerusalem, Jerusalem!" he was saying. "If you only realized, in this day, the things that make for peace! But now they are hidden from your eyes."

I did not know what he meant. But I knew he was not going to make himself a king.

Week for Remembrance

Early Monday morning I knocked on Zoldi's door. I had heard him stirring about since before dawn, and I knew he was troubled about what had happened the day before and about what might happen before the week was ended.

Most of the crowds would not return to their homes until sometime on the following Sunday. Passover time was always reason enough for a week of celebration in the city of Jerusalem and with the added spark of danger and excitement in the air, even the most frugal who realized the need to get back to their planting and plowing would not be willing to leave.

The village of Bethany had suddenly become a seething center of interest instead of a quiet mountain town. There were reports of other people who had been raised from the dead; there were those of Capernaum who were willing to swear that the small daughter of the ruler of the synagogue had been revived when all hope was gone. There were those from the tiny village of Nain, five miles southeast of Nazareth, who told of a widow's son, already in his bier and at the gates of the town on the way to the sepulchral caverns, who had been restored to life and given back to his mother.

This was different—this thing in Bethany. One could walk the two miles across the Mount of Olives and see a strong young man who had lain for four days in the grave. He would beat upon his breast with his strong fists. He would let one feel his hard muscles. He labored in the vineyard and plowed the vegetable garden like the strong men in the towns from which they came. He would throw back his head and laugh at the idea of people coming out from Jerusalem to look at him. "I was dead," he would say. "How can you doubt it? Do you not know Jesus, the Christ, the Son of God?"

The more enterprising in Bethany had set up stalls. They served cakes freshly baked in the heated stone vessels, and honey, and goats' milk. The neighbors wanted Martha to join them in their thriving business venture and prepare her date pudding. They suggested that she put her rue into small packages which could be carried in the purse. "You are his sister," they insisted. "You could make more money in this one week than you can make in a month with the produce cart." Martha would not. "It is like buying and selling in the Temple," she said. "Jesus would not want it so."

When Zoldi answered my knock, he looked tired and haggard. "You have not slept well either?" he asked.

I told him I was concerned about Jesus. I wanted to appoint myself as his personal bodyguard for the week, and I wanted Zoldi's approval.

"Good!" he agreed with enthusiasm. "I have considered one of the centurions for that duty but have hesitated to make the choice. You realize, do you not, that if rioting breaks out, those in close proximity to Jesus will be in grave danger?"

"I am sure of it, Zoldi," I answered, and again he looked at me strangely.

After a hurried breakfast, I went up on one of the parapets of the Tower Antonia. The tower itself was more than sixty-five feet high, and the great rock upon which it was built had an elevation of some seventy-five feet, so one looking out from the watch-towers had an excellent view of the entire city as well as of the Temple area below.

Everywhere things looked peaceful. It was April, and the sun was just beginning to spread its brightness over the dark green of the olive trees on the mountain which bore their name. Birds were singing like people at a country song-fest—each one louder than the other. All over the surrounding countryside, the early green figs were appearing on the fig trees. Springing out of the spaces between the stones of the Temple walls were the thick, hairy leaves of the hyssop plant which had an aromatic odor and a taste like peppermint. Growing everywhere, it seemed, were the brambles with their almost unbreakable branches and their sharp, cruel thorns which could cut into one's flesh like tiny daggers.

Far over to the west, past the amphitheater where the chariot races and the gladiatorial combats were held, was the palace of Herod with its huge, impregnable towers. Northward, between the first and the second north-city walls, the business district was coming alive. Merchants were beginning to place their wares outside, hoping that the visitors would be easier to snare, and the hordes of beggars were gathering to vie with each other for places of vantage where they might garner coins tossed to them by the passers-by.

I could imagine, as I turned my face to the east, that in the tiny village of Bethany, snuggled like a trusting child on the side of the Mount of Olives, my friends Martha and Mary and Lazarus were already digging around their vegetables, gathering their early figs, or perhaps starting across the mountain with their produce cart. I hoped fervently as I looked that Jesus was there with them or that he had left Judea and was making his way toward the comparative safety of Galilee.

I looked down into the Temple area and was impressed with its magnitude, as I always was when I surveyed it from this elevation. The massive walls which surrounded it must have been a full mile in circumference. On the inner side of the walls were beautiful porches with intricately carved and highly polished cedar ceilings. Monolithic columns of gleaming white stone separated each porch into wide aisles. The Royal Porch on the south wall had four rows of columns rather than the two which separated the others, and it had, in addition, two tall, covered gates whose steps led down to the street outside.

The porch on the east was designated as Solomon's Porch, and was supposed to have been a part of the temple built by King Solomon, and—some five hundred years ago—plundered and burned by the Babylonians. I had been told that this present temple was built by Herod the Great about the eighteenth year of his reign, not because he cared about the God of the Jews, but as a political gesture of good will.

The expansive outdoor area, called the Court of the Gentiles, was completely paved with immense stones. Here anyone who wished was permitted to enter and to make a prayer, but this was far from being true concerning the Temple proper. This three-storied edifice of white stone was surrounded by its own wall which the Jews called the triple wall of partition. It consisted of three parts—the wall of the temple building, as thick and heavy as the walls of a fortress, a lower outside wall four or five feet high, and connecting these two a flat terrace of ten or fifteen feet. Surrounding the lower wall were pillars on which were carved dire words of warning to any foreigner who might have the temerity to consider entering the Temple.

As a superior officer in the Roman army, I was not prohibited from entering, but knowing the strong feeling of the Jews against it, I should never have transgressed unless there was actual need for it. I felt that today might be one of those times. I made a careful note of the entrances. There were nine. The four on the north and the four on the south were tower-like structures heavily encrusted with silver and gold, and the one on the east, which was called the Gate Beautiful, was sheathed, not only with silver and gold, but with precious stones. Each day, I had been told, one hundred priests were assigned to open and close this door.

Outside the triple wall, on the southwest corner of the temple area, was the Council Chamber. This was the meeting place of the Sanhedrin. Looking down on it now, I saw something which made me forget the soft spring sunshine, the singing birds, the olive and fig trees, and the magnificence of the Temple. I saw a group of men filing out, standing for a moment as if in earnest conversation, and moving toward the Temple with determination evident in every step. Something told me that the delegation, sent from this early morning meeting, had something to do with Jesus.

I had never gone down the Tower stairs so fast. I entered the north gate, moved swiftly across the great paving stones to the Gate Beautiful which was just being opened, and entered into the Court of the Women. This was the lowest level of the inside portion. I climbed the fifteen steps leading to a portico across the front of the sacred inner part. There were no doors here, and one was able to see, above the twelve steps which ascended to the Court of the Priests, the great altar of unhewn stones, and back of it, the fabulous doors which guarded the Holy Place and the Holy of Holies. Nowhere in Rome or Athens or in the cities of Egypt had I seen anything to equal those doors. Even in my haste, I stopped still for a moment to look.

They were somewhere near one hundred feet high, and were hung with heavy draperies of blue and purple and scarlet. Surrounding the entire doorway, and encompassing the hangings, were golden vines from which suspended immense clusters of golden grapes. The vines, the leaves, and the grapes themselves were so skillfully executed that, except for the color and the size, one might have thought they were real.

I stood still for a moment longer in indecision. I wondered if I dared enter the Court of Israel intended only for male Jews, and then I held my breath in grave apprehension. Jesus came out of that court and began to climb the twelve steps to the Court of the Priests. Jesus—a peasant preacher from Galilee—would not be allowed there. If he dared to enter, trouble would begin—and quickly!

He did not go in. He stopped on the uppermost step. He would not break the smallest of the Jewish laws.

Crowds of tense, excited people had gathered now. They were on the wide portico, had filled the Court of the Women, and were pushing and thrusting each other aside as they tried to get through the Gate Beautiful from the Court of the Gentiles. Evidently word had gone out that Jesus was in the Temple. Many had seen him ride into the city on the previous day. Many had seen him as he had gone into the Temple and had driven out the traders just as I had seen him three years earlier on my first afternoon in Jerusalem.

Beggars always lay around the Gate Beautiful, asking alms of the people as they went in and out of the Temple. Not far away, northwest of the Tower Antonia, by the Sheep Gate, was the Pool of Bethesda. Around this pool five porticoes had been built for the benefit of the afflicted as the waters bubbled at certain times, and it was thought that they possessed healing power. All the beggars, all the afflicted, were trying now to make their way inside, hoping to see Jesus, hoping for a miracle.

Jesus had hardly turned his face to the crowd when I saw the delegation move in. They came out of the Court of the Priests and stood on the steps beside Jesus. He did not notice them. He began to teach, and his words were, as I always had found them, of far greater import than the miracles which he performed.

Suddenly I realized that it was the teaching of Jesus which the rulers feared. Miracles were not unknown in these eastern countries, but his words, his simple yet profound teachings, were something which the religious leaders could not combat.

They did not wait long—the deputation. They interrupted Jesus in the middle of a sentence.

"By what authority," they demanded sternly, "are you doing these things and who gave you this authority?"

There was sarcasm in their words and in their faces. I understood what they were saying, as did everyone who listened. They were saying that they were the authority here, that they were in control, and that he had received no permission from them to speak during this momentous occasion.

I knew that the Jews were a strict people, that noncomformity could be as monstrous a sin in their eyes as murder. I wondered how Jesus would answer so that the crowds would not turn against him, feeling that he had abrogated the rights which belonged to the religious element. As always, his wisdom was so far beyond their scheming cleverness that immediately he put them on the defensive. He put the important members of the delegation in the position in which they had planned to put him. He placed them in a position where they could not answer.

He replied to their questions without rancor.

"I will ask you a question," he said, "answer me, and I will tell you by what authority I do these things. Was the baptism of John the Baptist from heaven or from men?"

A simple question on the surface, but it put them in a quandary. John the Baptist was the latest of their prophets, and Jesus was making it plain that if they had not understood John, they would not be able to understand him. They were nonplussed. They drew aside a little to think things out. If they answered that John's baptism had been from heaven, then Jesus would ask why they had not believed him, and all men knew full well that John the Baptist had said publicly that it was Jesus of whom he spoke when he said, "He that comes after me is preferred before me." If they said that John's baptism was of men, the multitude would turn against them, for many believed John, and all held that he was a prophet. They had to make an answer. The crowd was quiet—waiting. "We do not know," they said.

Jesus resumed his teaching. He told them stories which touched their hearts, which stirred their thinking.

One was about a householder who planted a vineyard, set a hedge around it, dug a winepress in it, built a tower, let it out to tenants, and went into a far country. When harvest time came he sent servants to get the part of the fruits which were his, but the tenants beat one servant, stoned one, and killed one. This, Jesus told them, happened the second time, and the owner sent his own son, thinking they would respect him, but the tenants said to themselves, "This is the heir. We will kill him, and we will have the inheritance for ourselves."

"Then," Jesus said, solemnly, "they took the son, and cast him out of the vineyard, and put him to death!" He paused for a long moment, and the people waited.

"What will the owner of that vineyard do to those tenants when he comes?" he asked.

The whole multitude was with him now. They shouted, "He will kill those miserable tenants! He will let out his vineyard to other tenants who will give him the fruits which are his!"

I saw the look on the faces of the deputation. They knew the story was about them. They feared the crowd knew it too. They walked down those twelve steps with what dignity they could. They left the Temple, and I could see them making their way across the court to the council chamber. I felt sure they would be back—and they were.

This time it was not the priests who came. This time a group made up of the important members of two opposing parties, the Pharisees and the Herodians, entered and climbed the twelve steps to confront Jesus. A strange coalition indeed. Two parties diametrically opposed were holding firmly together on this question of retaining their security. They had decided upon a legal question which they felt sure would trap him, and they had decided upon a mere placating approach than the one used by the religious leaders.

One could almost believe them as they addressed Jesus with apparent courtesy and respect.

"Teacher," they said, "we know that you are true, and teach the way of God truthfully, and care for no man, for you do not regard the positions of men. Tell us, then, what do you think? Is it lawful to pay taxes to Caesar?"

They almost licked their lips in satisfaction. Now they would have him, they thought. This was something he could not escape. Let him answer that it was lawful for them to pay the tax, and the multitude would turn away from him because there was no subject which could stir more resentment than the taxes which they were forced by the publicans to pay to the Roman government.

If, on the other hand, he answered that the people need not pay, then all their problems would be solved for them; the Roman soldiers would be forced to arrest him as a traitor. I saw them looking at me triumphantly. It was as if they were saying, "Now! You have come here into our Temple, you Gentile, you Roman soldier; we will see to it that you have something to do!"

Jesus had not missed their obsequious approach or the malice which was back of their question.

"Why put me to the test, you hypocrites?" he asked. "Show me the money for the tax."

They handed him a coin rapidly enough. They felt sure he could not escape. "Whose likeness and inscription is this?" he asked, holding the coin high.

"Caesar's!" they shouted, confidently.

Jesus spoke so that not one person could miss his clear, convincing answer. "Render therefore to Caesar the things that are Caesar's, and to God the things that are God's."

They could not understand it. They marveled. Their fine plan had come to nothing—dismissed by a sentence. They could see that they themselves had lost standing with the crowds. There was complete silence for a moment.

Then it began to ripple, like a pebble dropped into the waters.

First a low chuckle here and there—then louder—then like a great wave the raucous laughter spread across the men's court, the portico, the Court of the Women, even outside in the Court of the Gentiles.

The second delegation left him, and went its way.

My heart was beating like a bird beating its wings against the bars of a cage. I knew Jesus' ability as a teacher. I knew his marvelous flair for storytelling, but for him to have been possessed of the ability to confound these well-prepared deputations of the most brilliant minds in Jerusalem, without effort on his part, set the blood rushing through my veins.

This was not the end. The aristocratic Sadducees made their erudite attempt. They came asking a ridiculous question about a woman married to one after another of seven brothers, and whose she would be in the resurrection. Jesus put his finger on the fallacy of their questioning as quickly and as easily as he had on the others. He knew, as everyone did, that the Sadducees did not believe in the resurrection from the dead, and his answer to them was simple—but potent.

"You are wrong, because you know neither the Scriptures nor the power of God."

I found myself thinking that perhaps that was the trouble with them all. Perhaps that might be the trouble with the whole wide world—we do not know the power of God.

Finally they gave up. The priests and rulers, the Pharisees and the Herodians, the patrician Sadducees, and the lawyers. They were unable to answer, and they did not dare to ask more questions.

I thought that the trouble was over at least for today. Jesus had not moved from his place on the top step. The people did not move toward the doors. The scribes and Pharisees stood waiting, and I realized as Jesus began to speak again that the trouble might only have begun. He addressed the crowds, and though there was no venom in his words, I could see that they were stinging like adders.

"The scribes and Pharisees," he said to the people, "sit on Moses' seat. Practice and observe whatever they tell you, but not what they do; for they preach, but do not practice."

The Pharisees and scribes began to leave, but before they reached the entrance, Jesus was addressing them, and although they seemed unwilling to remain, they stayed. They listened.

I felt that if he left the Temple alive, we could count it as a miracle. "Woe to you!" he repeated over and over, and with each woe, he literally piled up testimonies of their hypocrisies, their empty religion, and their empty hearts.

"Woe to you," he said. "You are blind guides, straining out a gnat and swallowing a camel! You cleanse the outside of the cup and the plate, but inside they are full of extortion and rapacity. You are like whitewashed tombs—beautiful on the outside, but inside full of dead men's bones. You are a brood of vipers!"

I placed my hand on the hilt of my sword. I wondered if the soldiers Zoldi had placed on guard would hear the disturbance and come in.

As suddenly as Jesus had begun his terrible words of judgment, he began to speak gently, with such yearning love for them in his voice that I could think of no comparison except a mother's tenderness as she might hold a rebellious child to her breast.

He held out his great, strong arms to them all—the scribes, the Pharisees, the Herodians, the Sadducees, those who wished to see him dead and those who loved him but understood him so dimly.

"O Jerusalem, Jerusalem!" he said. "How often would I have gathered your children together as a hen gathers her brood under her wings, and you would not!"

The people began to leave. They had understood the upbraiding and the thunderous words of stern judgment, but not this tender love which was for his enemies as well as his friends. This was beyond them. The old law of a tooth for a tooth and an eye for an eye was within their comprehension, but not this new law of loving their enemies and blessing those who despitefully used them.

It was beyond me also, and strangely enough, I felt a warm, glad glow in my heart that it was so. Jesus was beyond me! He was beyond me, and I was glad! The voice of thunder, I thought again, but also the voice of harpers playing on their harps!

As I walked across the Court of the Gentiles toward the Tower Antonia I could see that hundreds of Pharisees and

Sadducees were standing around the door to the Council Chamber. I felt sure they were planning another attack. I could see a
man trying to engage, first one and then the other in conversation,
but they all brushed him aside and continued their excited talking with each other.

It looked like the man Judas, but I knew I must be mistaken.

When I awoke on Tuesday morning, the rain was pouring down
outside my window in the Tower Antonia, and I thought I had
never been so grateful for rain in all my life. A cold spring rain,
I said to myself, could do more toward quieting enthusiasm, either
for crowning a new king, or putting a man to death, than an entire
legion of soldiers.

I was eager to talk to Mariamne again, and as soon as I had
finished my breakfast, I hurried to the house of Nicodemus. I reminded myself as I stood waiting for the servant to open the door
that the easy, relaxed life I had come to know in Capernaum was
quite different from the life in Jerusalem, and I wondered if my
eagerness might make me an embarrassingly early caller.

When I was taken into the reception room, however, I saw that
Matthew and Susanna were already there and that they were all
engaged in earnest conversation. As soon as the greetings were
over, Nicodemus urged Matthew to continue with what he had
been saying.

"I was telling them, Claudius," Matthew explained, "about what
happened yesterday afternoon after Jesus left the Temple. When
that gruelling session was ended, Jesus started walking out toward
the Mount of Olives. One of his followers has a beautiful garden
there which Jesus may use whenever he wishes. It is called
Gethsemane. It is so beautiful and so quiet that looking out over
the city below, one can almost forget the hatred and the plotting.

"For six months now, ever since Jesus took us away from the
push and bustle of the crowds to try to prepare us for the fact
that he must come to Jerusalem, he has been saying strange
things.

"He has been talking about being arrested, about suffering, and about dying. He has even talked about rising from the dead. We have attributed this to his constant fatigue, and have brushed it aside. But yesterday he named a day! It brought terror to our hearts, a terror from which we have not been able to escape. He spoke with such certainty that it was as if he was telling us something which was not new to him, something which he had known somewhere in the eternal councils of God.

"He spoke to us as if he were speaking to little children. 'You know that after two days the Passover is coming,' he said, 'and on that day the Son of man will be delivered up to be crucified.'"

"We all drew away from him in small, unbelieving groups," Matthew continued. "Crucified! A monstrous thing! We did not believe it, but we were afraid. Only one man seemed to believe Jesus. It was Judas. He had come out to the garden a little later than the rest, and when we told him what Jesus had said, he made a strange answer.

" 'Jesus is right,' he said, 'but he is wrong about the day.'

"We questioned him, but he would say nothing more."

Susanna dragged her heavy foot across the floor and moved over to Matthew's chair. She put her arm around his shoulder. She seemed to have trouble walking today.

"Matthew," Nicodemus said hesitantly, "I think I can tell you what it was that Judas meant, how he knew that Jesus was mistaken in thinking that the arrest and crucifixion if it should come, would not be on the feast day."

"You, sir! Do you know Judas?"

"Only by sight, and I could not have less desire to know him better. I dislike telling you, Matthew, but you men are harboring a serpent in your bosoms when you allow that man to remain as one of your number."

"Surely, sir, you must be mistaken."

"Not about this," Nicodemus said positively, and he began to tell a strange story.

Yesterday after Jesus had left the Temple and had gone out toward Gethsemane, the rulers, chagrined at the way their plans had been defeated, called a special meeting in the palace of the High Priest Caiaphas. They were determined to perfect plans from which Jesus could not possibly escape. For three years now, he had held up as mere sham their treasured rites and ceremonies, their incense burning, their solemn meetings, their long prayers in the market place.

"Jesus has shown," Nicodemus explained, "that the very things with which they have kept the people in subjection, so that they themselves could sit in the seats of the mighty, are shoddy, threadbare garments which the rulers draw about themselves to conceal their insincerities. 'Ravening wolves in sheeps' clothing,' he has called them."

I interrupted to ask a question. "How is it, Nicodemus, if those who are in control hate him so intensely—and fear what he can do—they have not arrested him on some spurious charge? Why is it they have not conspired to have him murdered? I myself have seen the most brutal murder done in the presence of many people and no word of it ever brought before the courts."

"It is because of the love which people hold in their hearts for Jesus, Claudius. People from every walk of life, the rich, the poor, the educated, the illiterate—people from Beersheba to Dan—love Jesus, and the rulers know it. They dare not arrest him except by stealth. They dare not put him to death without some semblance of legality back of their actions. I am sure you refer to John the Baptist, but although he had a great following, he never was a man to love."

Nicodemus resumed his account of the events of the previous afternoon. The members of the Sanhedrin, he said, sitting in session in the palace of Caiaphas, had been disturbed by a commotion. Only members might enter, and they were curious. At the door they saw a man, distraught but determined, fighting his way past the guards and into the room. It was Judas.

"Let me in!" he insisted. "Let me get through to the high priest! I have something he will want to hear!"

Caiaphas had motioned for the guards to release him and let him speak.

Judas did not waste time. It was as if he dared not delay lest he lose his courage. "What will you give me if I will deliver him to you?" he demanded.

He did not call Jesus by name, but the high priest answered him with eagerness. The entire assembly leaned forward in their

seats. This was beyond all their hopes and plans! One of Jesus'
own followers who would conspire with them, would come for
the arresting soldiers when the crowds were not around and when
there was no tumult among the people.

"Thirty pieces of silver!" Caiaphas shouted excitedly.

It was the price of a slave in the open market. Judas took it
and left.

As he reached the door, Caiaphas had the guards call him back.
"One stipulation!" he said. "The arrest must not be on the feast
day!"

Nicodemus looked at Matthew sadly. "Matthew," he said,
"your friend Judas is a traitor."

In Matthew's eyes there was the befuddled look of one who
has suddenly relinquished treasured hopes and dreams.

Mariamne and Susanna were sobbing unrestrainedly. I left,
and went back to the tower.

The clouds hung low over the city, and over my heart. I thought
of those rulers in the palace of the high priest and how explicit
their directions had been, how determined they were that Jesus
should not be arrested on the feast day.

I thought of Jesus, standing out on a mountainside, having no
religious or political prestige, having none of the things men count
great, saying to a little group of nondescript men, "After two days
the Passover is coming, and the Son of man will be delivered up."

I wondered who was in control.

I dreaded for the sun to go down on Thursday night. I dreaded
for Friday to come.

+   +   +

The sun shone out just after noon on Thursday. I counted
the hours until I would see it sink in the western sky. At that
moment, the great day—the feast day—the initiation of the week's
celebration would begin.

I looked out over the city and thought to myself that if in that
multitude of Jewish worshipers there should be a Gentile, a
stranger from Corinth or Athens or Philippi or Rome, passing
through on business or as a tourist, knowing little of the Jewish
religion, he would be astonished at the crowds pushing and

jostling each other as they tried to make up for the hours lost by the rain. He never would have believed, I told myself, that underneath the ebullience, the holiday spirit, the religious fervor, there surged the ugly, elemental emotions of hatred and envy and treachery and fear.

I thought that if he should find someone who had the time to point out the places of interest, he would have been shown the magnificent palace of Caiaphas, the high priest, and looking at its imposing facade, he would never have suspected that closeted inside were the men who were the important participants of this religious celebration, the highest of the religious dignitaries, the wealthy and aristocratic, the intelligentsia of Jerusalem. Seeing them coming out of the palace and filing by in full regalia, as they made their way solemnly toward the Temple, he would have thought that their sacrifices and their ceremonies were the matters to which they had been giving their careful consideration. The visitor never would have suspected that they were planning the death of an innocent man.

As I left the Tower Antonia, I saw that guards were standing on both staircases, and as I passed through the north gate into the Temple area, I noted the careful manner in which Zoldi had stationed fully armed soldiers so that they could come together quickly in case of a riotous move. The Temple seemed quiet enough, however, with only a group of priests standing outside the Gate Beautiful. Their conversation ceased completely as I passed by, convincing me that ominous plans were still afoot.

The afternoon began to wane, and one could feel the change in the city. The sun was going down, and a new day was about to begin. The streets and bazaars became almost empty. The shopkeepers hurriedly pushed their wares inside the doors. The beggars pocketed the few scattered coins and disappeared. Visitors hastened to their tents outside the city gates or to the homes of friends and kinsfolk who had invited them to partake of the Passover supper. It was the hour for the slaying of the lamb which would be eaten with bitter herbs and unleavened bread and wine mixed with water.

Tomorrow the sacrificial lambs would be slain in the Temple, tomorrow—the feast day. "On the feast day, I shall be put to

death," Jesus had told Matthew and the others. My mind searched
for the words of John the Baptist, "Behold the Lamb of God!"
I wondered if it all fit together, but I did not know the answer.

+   +   +

It seemed I hardly had been asleep at all, when before the
dawn on Friday morning there was a resounding knock on my
door. I leaped from my bed, certain that the trouble had started
and that Zoldi was summoning me to my place of duty.

It was Matthew. His face was old, and white, and stark in terror. He sat down on my bed, shaking. I wrapped a blanket around
his shoulders and poured him a glass of wine, but his hands would
not hold it. He began to sob. I had never seen a strong man cry.
His words were unintelligible as he repeated them over and over
again, and for awhile I feared that his mind must be gone.

At last I understood him. "We all deserted him and fled," he
was saying. "We all deserted him and fled."

"Tell me, Matthew," I said, placing an arm about his shoulders,
"is it about Jesus? We must not waste time if he needs our help."

"It is too late! It is too late! They have taken him before the
Sanhedrin! They will put him to death!"

"Think quietly, sir," I urged him. "You know the Sanhedrin
does not meet at night. It is only beginning to dawn. The roosters
have not yet begun to crow."

He grew more calm. He began to talk. His words were sometimes garbled and incoherent, but the picture he drew was clear
and plain.

Yesterday, all day, he had been troubled. He felt he should go
to Jesus and tell him what Nicodemus had said about Judas. He
felt he ought to confide in the men. He convinced himself that it
would only grieve Jesus to know that Judas had gone to the rulers
offering to help them. He told himself that if he spoke to the
men, there might be dissension and fighting in the little group.
He knew the quick tempers of John and James, how they had
been called the sons of thunder, and Peter's impetuosity. Matthew
told me that he was a little afraid of Judas, that sometimes he had
a mean look.

Late in the afternoon Jesus had taken them to a quiet room in the poorer section of town so that they might eat the Passover supper together. There, Matthew said, his fears and uncertainties had disappeared. He thought he had done what was right, that nothing should have disturbed that sacred meal. He searched the face of Judas, and comforted himself that Nicodemus must have been wrong.

Suddenly all his forebodings seemed to fill his throat. He could not swallow the food which was in his mouth. Jesus was speaking quietly, but there was a look of infinite sorrow on his face, and it was as if Matthew knew the words before they were spoken. "One of you," Jesus said, "is going to betray me."

The men thought Jesus spoke a parable. They asked, "Is it I? Is it I?" but only to hear his reassuring words.

At Peter's urging, John asked plainly, "Who is it?"

Jesus spoke to Judas. "Whatever you do," he said, "do it quickly!"

Matthew began to sob. "They did not understand!" he said. "They thought Jesus spoke of the money bag which Judas carried. If only I had told them then about the thirty pieces of silver, they would never have let Judas leave the room. They would never have let him go out into the night. I could have saved Jesus' life!"

"Go on, Matthew," I urged him, "tell me what happened then."

As if nothing had happened, Jesus started talking to them. He talked gently, patiently, as if they had been little children. Knowing that Judas had gone to betray him, he spoke to them of joy, of peace, and of an untroubled heart.

After they had sung the Passover hymn, they started walking out across the Kidron Valley toward the Mount of Olives. They had supposed they were going to Bethany, but Jesus went only as far as the mountain, to the garden called Gethsemane. He went forward a little alone, and began to pray. The men fell down upon the grass, and almost immediately were fast asleep.

Matthew could not rest. He tossed from side to side. He sat up, and looked out into the darkness. He wondered if he should go to Jesus, back there in the fastnesses of the garden, praying. He wished they were armed other than with Peter's cheap sword.

"I was afraid," Matthew said, "and suddenly I knew that there was reason for my fears. From down the mountain came the sinister, ominous rumbling of a marching mob. We were all on our feet in an instant, and through the olive trees we could see them coming. It was a terrifying thing to see! At the head of a band of Roman soldiers which the rulers must have commandeered from the city guards and some riffraff who were carrying swords and sticks and waving lanterns in the darkness, was Judas. He came forward, and kissed Jesus on the cheek.

"Jesus spoke to him gently. He said, 'Friend, why are you here?'

"Judas looked at Jesus as if he had no memory of his face."

Jesus had gone out then, Matthew told me, to where the light from the lanterns showed his face plainly. "Whom do you seek?" he asked.

"Jesus of Nazareth!" the soldiers answered—and the rabble waving their sticks and staves.

Jesus answered simply, "I am he!"

"I tell you, Claudius," Matthew said, excitedly, "when Jesus spoke it was like a terrific wave had swept across them all. Judas, the Roman soldiers, and the street rabble! They all fell back as if he had struck them!

"Again Jesus asked them, 'Whom do you seek?' When they answered, he replied, 'I told you that I am he; so, if you seek me, let these men go.'

"I suppose it broke Peter's heart to see Jesus trying to save us. He took out his sword, and he cut off the ear of one of the servants of the high priest. It was a futile, foolish thing to do, and I was surprised that the soldiers did not cut him down, but it was something, Claudius! It was something out of all the brave words we all had spoken as we came out across the Kidron Valley only an hour or so ago.

"Jesus had said to us, 'You will all fall away because of me this night,' but Peter had said stoutly, 'The others, perhaps, but not I!' 'Peter, before the cock crows,' Jesus told him, 'you will deny me three times,' and Peter had answered vehemently, 'Even if I must die with you, I will not deny you.' And Claudius, we all echoed Peter's thoughts.

"But Peter's one gesture was the end of our concerted bravery.

The soldiers rushed forward then, and bound Jesus. They bound him—an unarmed man, defended only by trembling, unarmed men, except for Peter's ineffective sword. They bound him, and led him away as if they were afraid."

Suddenly Matthew's emotion swept over him again. He began to sob, "We all forsook him! We all forsook him, and fled!"

I took him by the arm, and lifted him up. "Control yourself, sir," I told him sternly. "We must go at once to find Jesus."

As Matthew had talked, it had occurred to me that if their plans had suddenly been altered, it was possible the Sanhedrin could be in session at this moment in spite of their law against it.

We hurried down the tower stairs, but when we came to the Council Chamber, the doors were closed and locked. I remembered what Nicodemus had told us about the meeting in the palace of the high priest, and we turned our steps toward that section of the city.

It was barely beginning to be light, and the streets were deserted. After the celebration of the night before, most of the residents of Jerusalem were still asleep. Even the beggars were waiting until the crowds began milling around before they took up their stations on the street corners and around the Temple gates.

When we reached the exclusive residential section where the palace stood it was easy to see that something unusual was taking place. Lights were shining from all the windows, and around the gate to the courtyard, crowds were beginning to gather. I was afraid Matthew might be in danger if he went inside, and I suggested that he wait, but his courage was high now, and he insisted upon following closely after me as I entered the court.

A biting, penetrating chill was in the early spring morning, and I could see that the servants of the high priest had built a fire in the center of the yard, and were standing around it, holding out their hands to its warmth.

Standing with them, warming himself, was Peter.

He glanced at Matthew and at me, and then looked away as if he did not wish to be associated with us. In some way, however, he attracted the attention of the little servant girl who had opened the gate for us, and she called out suddenly as if she had made an important discovery. Pointing at Peter, she said with excitement in her voice, "You were with this Jesus of Nazareth!"

The conversation in the courtyard stopped. They all looked at Peter. I felt, rather than saw, Matthew step outside the gate. I heard Peter answer in a mumbling voice, "I do not know what you mean."

He moved uneasily away from the brightness of the fire into the dim light of the porch, but there another servant took up the accusations. "You are a Galilean!" she declared positively. "I can tell by the way you talk! You were with Jesus and those men!"

I saw the panic in Peter's face. I heard him say—louder this time —"I was not!"

Standing near him on the porch was one of the menservants of the high priest, and he moved close to Peter and peered into his face. He raised his arm menacingly and shouted, "Did I not see you back there in the Garden of Gethsemane? Are you not the one who cut off the ear of my kinsman Malchus? You were with Jesus!"

Now Peter lost all self-control. He was possessed by terror, and he also began to shout. He began to curse and to swear. He said, "I do not know the man!"

Over on the edge of the courtyard a rooster crowed.

At that moment the great doors of the palace opened, and the high priest, the chief priests, and the elders came out. In their midst was Jesus. His face was bruised, and had been spit upon. His hands were bound. Yet I saw in him high dignity and kingly poise. He seemed unaware of the dignitaries who surrounded him. His attention was directed toward one fearful follower who, for a time, had lost, not his faith, but his courage.

Jesus turned and looked at Peter.

In that look there was nothing of condemnation. There was in it gentleness, understanding, and great compassion.

Big, strong, blustering Peter went over to the wall of the courtyard, put his head in his arms, and wept bitterly.

The members of the Sanhedrin who had lingered on the inside of the palace now marched out into the courtyard. They were nodding their heads as they talked, and satisfaction was plastered like a gruesome mask on their faces. One could tell they thought they had done a good early morning's work. They were sure their easy and profitable positions were no longer in jeopardy. Even if I had not seen the bruises and the spit, I would have known by their smug faces that it had not gone well for Jesus.

I wondered why Nicodemus had not been there to meet with the court, and then I saw him coming out of the door in close conversation with his friend, Joseph of Arimathea. As soon as he caught sight of me, he walked casually to where I was standing, and as he passed, said in a low voice, "Wait for a moment, Claudius, and then come to my home. I have much I wish to tell you, but with the Sanhedrin in its present mood, it will be better for us both if we are not seen walking together."

I knew that Nicodemus was not a fearful man, and his caution made me realize the intensity of feeling which was rampant among those rulers of the Jewish people, and it also made me more convinced than ever that Nicodemus would never do anything which would cause him to lose his treasured place as jurist and educator in Jerusalem. I thought of Mariamne and of how closely knit her own life was with the lives of her father and mother.

I knew that the girl I had come to love so dearly was forever separated from me by an insurmountable wall of tradition.

Jesus had been arrested, hit in the face, and spit upon.

His own men had all deserted him and fled. Judas had betrayed him to his enemies. Peter had denied three times that he ever knew him. Matthew's one small spurt of courage had flickered out like a candle in the wind.

I had never felt more desolate.

When I reached Nicodemus' house, I seemed to sense the tension the moment the servant opened the door. "Come in quickly," he said.

The great reception room was empty, and as he led the way up the stairs to the summer parlor, an upper room above the rooftop which was used only by the family, he seemed to be walking on tiptoe lest he be heard, and when he spoke it was almost in a whisper.

I saw that Nicodemus and his wife, with Mariamne and Joseph, had their chairs drawn close together, and Mariamne's dark eyes were dimmed with tears.

Nicodemus greeted me cordially and had the servant draw a chair for me near the group. They seemed reluctant to continue their conversation, and since I was deeply concerned about Matthew, I asked if they had seen him. He had come by only for a moment, they told me, to take Susanna to the shoemaker who fashioned the heavy shoe she wore on her right foot. Dear Susanna, I thought, remembering the pride she felt in the thump! thump! thump! of her clumsy foot because it seemed to set forth the faith which was in her heart, the faith which depended upon nothing except her belief in Jesus.

"Claudius," Nicodemus said, speaking slowly, "it is only because of your position in the Roman army and because I feel we may need your help before this day is ended that I asked you to follow me here, that Joseph and I are persuaded to expose to you the unprecedented behavior of our own people, our own friends. Even now we find it difficult to believe."

As they began to tell the things which had taken place in the early morning hours, I too found it hard to believe. I knew, however, that in the report of these two men there was nothing of exaggeration, no striving for dramatic effects. The words they spoke were hard words of truth, and it was as if every one of them was spoken with effort, and with reluctance.

It had started early in the morning, before the dawn—those hours when Matthew was sobbing in my quarters. Joseph and Nicodemus had been aroused from their sleep by a messenger from Caiaphas, the high priest, demanding that they report to his palace immediately for an important meeting of the Sanhedrin. The full council was expected, the man stated positively.

This was an unheard-of procedure. The Jewish law forbade the gathering of that body except in the daylight hours. Nicodemus had drawn the curtains of his room and had seen that there was no light in the eastern sky. Joseph had listened, and no roosters were crowing. They were perturbed and uncertain, but they went. One does not disobey.

They saw at once that the full assembly was in session. This too was unusual. Except in cases of utmost importance, only enough members came together to form a quorum, yet they were all there —the entire seventy members, and the daylight had not yet come. There was unusual solemnity there, as if they had met to stand together against some majestic force which was beyond their comprehension, as if, Nicodemus had thought, Palestine had been attacked by a gigantic army from an unknown country.

When they were seated, Joseph had whispered to the council member who sat beside him, asking if he had any idea as to the reason for the meeting.

"I know," the man had answered. "I live quite near the palace of Annas, father-in-law to Caiaphas. It was immediately after the messenger had summoned me here that I heard an excited crowd gathered around the gate to Annas' villa. I joined them, and slipped into the house. Knowing the old man rather well, I expected the servants to be brandishing swords and driving us out before he was awakened. Strangely enough, Annas himself opened the door, motioned us into the great library, and seated himself in a high-backed chair as if he were a judge about to try an important case.

"As he pounded on the floor with his cane for silence, I caught sight of the prisoner. I decided at once that it must be the young teacher, Jesus. I was overwhelmed with amazement. He was bound hand and foot, and yet he stood so tall, so enveloped in his own calm and dignity that I had the feeling it was he who was the judge, and not old Annas. I had the feeling that if he desired, he could turn his back on the lot of us, walk out the door, and none of us would have the power to stop him.

"Annas himself seemed uncertain. He began to ask Jesus some inconsequential questions concerning how many followers he had, and what the nature of his teaching had been. Jesus answered Annas—with the respect due his age and position—that he always had taught openly, that he never had taught in secret. He suggested that Annas ask those who had heard him.

"A Roman officer, probably hoping to gain favor with the old man, slapped Jesus across the face with the palm of his hand. A wide streak showed on the deep bronze of Jesus' cheek, and he answered quietly, 'If I have spoken wrongly, bear witness to the wrong, but if I have spoken rightly, why do you strike me?'

"The officer had put his hand to his own cheek as if he were the one who had been struck, and Annas seemed to lose interest in the case. 'It is about this Jesus,' the man whispered to Joseph, 'that we are here.' "

Nicodemus had also spoken to the man seated beside him and this man also had an answer. He had arrived early, and had heard a discussion between the high priest and one of the elders.

While Caiaphas sat at the celebration of the Passover supper on the previous evening, the man Judas had come pounding on his door. He said that Jesus and his followers were starting out across the Kidron Valley toward the garden called Gethsemane, that he would take an arresting party now or not at all. He was distraught, cracking his knuckles and mumbling, "Whatever I do, I must do quickly."

Caiaphas had been much perturbed, but had felt he did not dare to lose the help of this man who seemed on the verge of a sudden reversal of attitude. He sent aides to form an arresting party and to bring the witnesses who had been hired by the Sanhedrin to testify against Jesus.

Nicodemus said that it was while these two whispered conversations were being carried on that Jesus was brought into the room, and that as deeply as he had come to believe in him as the Christ, the Son of God, he had not been prepared to witness the strange blending of gentleness and of power which he saw.

The high priest was obviously flustered, hurried, and unsure of himself, as were the members of the Sanhedrin, but there was no evidence of anything other than calmness and strength in the prisoner.

It was the custom, Nicodemus and Joseph agreed, for the president of the court to state the case against the accused as the first order of business, but immediately Caiaphas began to call the witnesses. Every man in the room was cognizant of the reason. The high priest had no case to state, no accusation to make.

The testimony of the witnesses would not hang together. Some said one thing, some another, but Caiaphas would not give up. Finally he found two who were willing to swear the same thing.

"This fellow," they declared under oath, "said, 'I am able to destroy the temple of God and to build it in three days.'"

They all knew the charge was ridiculous, that it should have been laughed out of court, but it was all they had. Now, they seemed to feel, there was a charge against the prisoner! Now he would be compelled to answer! But Jesus answered them not a word.

Caiaphas was infuriated. "Why do you not answer?" he lashed out venomously at Jesus. "Do you not hear what they are saying against you?"

He moved out of his seat then, the seat of the president of the Supreme Court of the Jewish people. He walked across the room, stood directly in front of Jesus, leaned forward until his face was almost in Jesus' own, and shouted as if he were standing a long way off. He was going to force the prisoner to speak! He was putting him under legal oath, the legal oath of the Sanhedrin, with which all Jews were familiar.

"I adjure you by the living God, tell us if you are the Christ, the Son of God."

The question which the high priest had asked hung in the air like a living thing.

Jesus knew the law, he knew the sacredness of the Hebrew oath, and he answered.

Only two words, but they changed the court room into a frenzied mob. The high priest began to tear his robe although he knew full well the law against it. He tore the ephod made of gold and blue and scarlet and of fine twined linen. He tore the breastplate clasped at the shoulder by onyx stones.

Jesus spoke as if he stated a simple fact. He spoke quietly, and yet it was as if he spoke to each man there—as an individual.

Two words he spoke in answer to the high priest's question.

"I am," he said.

"What need have we now of further witnesses?" came the triumphant harshness of the high priest's voice. "You have heard what he said! This is blasphemy! What is your verdict?"

"He deserves death!" they shouted.

There was not one man in the Council Chamber who did not know that the law forbade them to pass sentence on the same day in which a prisoner had been arrested. But they were primitive men now, fighting for their security and caring nothing as to how their aims were accomplished.

Suddenly, they too left their seats.

They rushed at Jesus as if he had been the basest, most dangerous criminal, armed to the teeth. They passed him where he stood, and as they passed they would buffet him with their shoulders. One whipped out a scarf and tied it around his eyes.

"I think they could not bear the look that was in them," Nicodemus told us. "If Jesus had had in his face a look of disdain, or of arrogance, or even that of a victim about to die for a lost cause, I think they could have borne it, but the look of deep sorrow and of love for us all they could not bear to look upon."

After they had blindfolded him, Joseph told us, they grew bolder. They began to hit him with their hands, and to spit in his face as they passed by. One of them shouted, "Prophesy to us, you Christ! Who is it that struck you?"

They all took up the cry. It was clever. It made them feel surer of themselves. "If you are the Christ," they screamed, "prophesy! Who is it that struck you?"

Finally their wrath was spent. They knew that they must get on with the trial before the day was too far gone and the crowds began to gather. They must take him now to Pilate.

A great stroke of good fortune, they said to each other, that Pilate was in Jerusalem for the feast since the sentence of death could not be executed until the case had been reviewed and passed upon by the Roman procurator. Pilate, having his quarters in the Galilean Embassy, had tried two dangerous criminals only yesterday, and they were to be crucified before this day ended. They must get Jesus to Pilate.

Nicodemus and Joseph had come to the end of their story. Nicodemus put his head on his arms on a nearby table. Joseph walked over and put his hand on the shoulder of his friend. Mariamne was in the arms of her mother sobbing softly.

We heard the opening of the huge bronze door, and the thump! thump! of Susanna's new shoe as she and Matthew came up the stairs. One look at their faces told me that they already knew the story which I had just heard.

I realized that my duty was at the Embassy, and as I left I heard Matthew saying, "Now they have assembled a huge mob like those who were in the Garden last night. All the riffraff of Jerusalem will have money in their pockets this day."

When I came to the Embassy which was on the northwest corner of the upper city, the members of the Sanhedrin were standing on the outside with the rabble behind them, and Jesus was nowhere to be seen. At first I wondered if perhaps Pilate had refused to allow them to enter, but knowing his eagerness to retain their good will, I doubted this probability, and then I remembered a strange Jewish law which I had included in my article on Jewish religion. A Jew, having put foot on Gentile soil or having entered any building occupied by Gentiles on the great day of the Passover Feast was not allowed to take part in the ceremonies which were to follow, and so careful were they—the religious leaders, the legislative and executive body of the people of Palestine—lest they offend in some small letter of the law, because in this Embassy Pilate had erected golden shields of honor to Tiberius, the Roman Emperor, and because it was more often called the House of Procurators than the Palace of Herod, they would not go in.

In my home in Athens, on a hill west of the Acropolis, where the Areopagus stood, my father and I attended many meetings of the High Court. We had seen many strange trials, but never one so strange as this. Here the prosecuting attorneys, who were themselves the accusers, were standing outside the building. The accused was on the inside, and the judge must go back and forth between them. I did not doubt that this was as great a travesty on justice as ever would be recorded in the annals of legal history.

As I watched, I saw that Pilate had had his curule brought onto a small balcony which projected from one of the windows of his quarters overlooking the tribunal below it where the procurators who had preceded him had often sentenced men to scourging and to crucifixion. I wondered if those who stood on the flagstones which paved the open court between the palace and the wall

which separated it from the city felt protected—even righteous—
because they were obeying the minutest detail of their sacred
law. I wondered also, as I looked at their hard, determined faces,
if their God looked down on them in sorrow.

Suddenly and unaccountably, my mind went back to the old
farmer up in Galilee who had stood with his hand on his plow,
his long beard blowing in the wind, declaring the words of the
prophet,

> "They hire a goldsmith, and he makes it into a god;
>   then they fall down and worship!
> They lift it upon their shoulders, then carry it,
>   they set it in its place, and it stands there;
>   it cannot move from its place.
> If one cries to it, it does not answer or save him from his
>   trouble."

I knew the crowd outside the palace on this early Friday morning were worshiping their idols as surely as if they were idols
which one could see. I knew that the rich and powerful were
falling down before their wealth and power, and that the rabble—
rattling their coins in their pockets, waiting for the signal from the
priests and elders—cared nothing about which way they shouted
as long as they could touch those precious coins and fall down
before their own small shrines.

As the trial seemed about to begin, Pilate caught sight of me,
and to my amazement he beckoned for me to join him on the balcony. My appointment with him was for Friday afternoon, and
I wondered if he planned now to use it as an excuse for dismiss-
ing the Sanhedrin. As soon as I reached him I saw in his face and
in his demeanor the same fearfulness and insecurity I had observed on earlier occasions. I realized that Pilate despised the
men who were demanding that he perform his duty as a procurator, and yet he did not dare refuse their demands.

My eyes fixed as if in fascination on the great gold and amethyst
ring. His right hand was waving back and forth now in the same
aimless, futile gesture I had seen on the night of Herod's birthday
party as Herodias was shouting for the head of John the Baptist,
and Herod was maintaining with drunken dignity that he must

abide by his oath. I remembered with sickening vividness the imprint of that ring on the temple of the poor dead Julius.

"Come inside for a moment, Tribune," Pilate said. "I wish to ask if in your travels over Palestine you have gained pertinent information concerning this Jesus of Nazareth. Many strange rumors are abroad. It is said that Herod, believing this man to be John the Baptist returned from the dead to haunt him, has lost much weight. I am told that he trembles when Jesus' name is mentioned. For some reason I am loath to try this young teacher. Give me an opinion, Tribune. You are not a Jew with peculiar ideas of a coming Messiah, nor are you an excitable man. Tell me what you think."

I had felt amazement when Pilate had motioned for me to come to him on the balcony. I was amazed that he asked for my opinion. My amazement at these things, however, did not compare with the amazement I felt at my own answer, the answer of Tribune Claudius Lysias, pagan, Gentile, philosopher by inheritance. It was almost as if I heard the voice of someone other than myself.

"I believe you will have no power over him, sir. I believe that this trial, and the outcome of this day, is completely in his hands."

"You believe this, Tribune?"

"I believe it, sir."

"Then stay here with me. Stand just inside the judgment hall where you will not be seen by those obsequious, scheming Jews."

Pilate stepped back onto the balcony, and I turned my eyes to the man in the dimly lighted room. Jesus stood smiling at me, and there was in his eyes the same look of welcome which I had seen on that day when I had sailed with him on the Sea of Galilee. For almost three years some vague need, some yearning for wisdom and power beyond my own, had stirred in my heart. The philosophy of my father would not quiet its urgency, nor pagan gods produce an answer which could satisfy. Many a time I had told myself if Jesus had the answer, that answer would come as the result of some stupendous miracle greater than any I had witnessed, some cataclysmic occurrence which would drive from my mind forever all doubt and all uncertainty.

Yet there he stood, surrounded by the power of the Roman Empire, in the midst of Jewish power and might—a prisoner—and

I realized, as I knew he did, that this welcome was far deeper and more significant than the welcome on the boat.

This was the welcome of a father for a son who had been in a far country, and had come home.

"If you need me, sir, I am here to defend you."

+　　+　　+

The trial was starting now. Pilate was shouting to the group outside—the chief priests, and the elders of the people with their waiting mob behind them—"What accusations do you bring against this man?"

There was a moment's pause. This was the thing which troubled them most. They had no just accusation, and they evaded the question. Their words fairly dripping with respect for the Roman procurator's importance and his busy schedule, they answered, "If this man were not an evildoer, we would not have handed him over."

I could see the relief on Pilate's face. They had no accusation against Jesus, and so he could refuse to take the case. He answered them bluntly, turning away even as he spoke, "Take him yourself. You are the Jewish tribunal. Take him and judge him by your own law."

But they were not to be dismissed so easily, and they shouted frantically, before Pilate could enter the palace and be lost to them, "But it is not lawful for us to put any man to death!"

There it was! In the open now, their nefarious plan! They had brought a man here to be sentenced to death!

Pilate waved his right hand back and forth, his eyes on the ring. He knew he needed help, but he found none. He must turn back to their demands, and he must hear the case to the end, but he only made a gesture which told them to wait, and he went into the judgment hall. I wondered if he felt he might get help from the prisoner himself. He walked slowly like an old man trying to make up his mind but lacking the ability to assemble the pertinent facts.

I realized that Pilate had never before been face to face with Jesus, and I could see his surprise when he looked at him. He was accustomed, no doubt, to cringing, trembling prisoners, begging for mercy, to arrogant, defiant criminals, daring him to do his worst, but I could see that this straight, king-like young man who stood waiting quietly for his decision, was something for which he had not been prepared.

Pilate asked a direct question. "Are you the king of the Jews?" Jesus answered with a question of his own. "Do you say this of your own accord, or did others say it to you about me?"

I could hardly keep from calling out to this troubled, insecure man, "That is the important question, Pilate! I have only this day found the answer for myself. It is not what I may have been told by Matthew, or Lazarus, or Susanna, or even one so dear to me as Mariamne. It is what I myself believe about Jesus which is of paramount importance. It is what every man must ask, and answer for himself." But I knew that unless Pilate addressed me, I had no right to speak.

Pilate was angry now. I could tell that he felt he had not received the cringing respect which he craved and demanded. "Am I a Jew?" he asked Jesus with biting sarcasm. "Your own people have brought you here! What have you done?"

Jesus answered Pilate. He said quietly, "My kingdom is not of this world. If my kingship were of this world, my servants would fight, that I might not be handed over to the Jews."

"Are you a king, then?" Pilate insisted.

"For this cause I was born, and for this I have come into the world, to bear witness to the truth."

Pilate turned away. "What is truth?" he asked bitterly.

I wanted to help Pilate. I wanted to tell Pilate that I believed Jesus, even though I had come to that belief the long, hard way of a Gentile and a pagan, as he was himself a Gentile and a pagan, but I knew I could not reach him. I felt relieved, however, because I thought the trial was ended. I was certain Pilate had seen that these leaders of the Jews lacked a legal accusation against Jesus and that now he was going to step out on the balcony and render the verdict. He did. He stepped out, and held up his hand, and there was immediate quiet.

"I find no crime in this man!" he said with conviction and with finality.

I told myself that the day I had dreaded had been a glorious one. I had come at last to know Jesus as he was. The trial was over; the verdict of "not guilty" had been rendered. I thought that I must hurry to find Mariamne and Nicodemus and the others, to tell them they had nothing to fear. Only a moment passed, however, before the strident voices of the rulers again came crashing into the judgment hall.

"He stirs up the people! He says he is king! He says we ought not to pay taxes to Caesar! He teaches these things from Galilee to Jerusalem!"

They lied. Only Monday I had stood in their Temple as they asked him question after question, trying to trap him, and I had heard him say plainly, "Render to Caesar the things which are Caesar's, and to God the things which are God's." They were progressing now, I thought. At first they had hired witnesses to do their lying for them.

Pilate knew that he was trapped, that he dare not hold to his own verdict. If these men reported to Vitellius of Syria that he had released a man who was a traitor to the Roman government, who incited the populace to refuse to pay their tribute, then his whole career would be at an end. One thing he had heard in the shouting had given him hope. It was the mention of the province of Galilee. Pilate knew that his old enemy Herod was in Jerusalem for the Passover Feast. If he could turn the whole case to Herod, it would give Herod a feeling of importance which might cement their strained relations, and he himself could be rid of this trial evidently instigated by envious conspirators.

He turned to me for the first time. "Is this Jesus a native of Galilee?" he asked, and when I answered in the affirmative, he ordered that Jesus be taken into Herod's apartment. The chief priests and the elders and the rabble waited. I wanted to go with Jesus. I did not trust Herod. But I could see that Pilate expected me to remain with him. He was wiping the perspiration now from his hands and his face, and he had slumped forward into the same position I remembered on the day of my first interview with him when he had told me how he hated the position as procurator, and how the ambition of his wife was like a whip across his back.

Claudia will never allow him to release Jesus, I thought, she will see Jesus hanging on a Roman cross rather than give up her high position.

Pilate's relief was shortlived. A guard entered and handed him a note, and when he had read it, he rose, and with a shrug of resignation, began to address the people. Jesus was standing beside him now.

"Hear me!" Pilate shouted, his voice high and shrill. "You brought me this man as one who was perverting the people; and after examining him before you, I did not find him guilty of any of your charges against him; nor did Herod, for he sent him back to us. Behold, nothing deserving death has been done by him. I will therefore chastise him and release him. You know well that on this day each year, the Roman government releases one of your own people. Today I will release Jesus of Nazareth!"

The third verdict, I thought to myself. The third time the decision of "not guilty" has been handed down, twice by Pilate, the highest official of the Roman government in Palestine, and once by their own Tetrarch of Galilee, the home province of Jesus.

But I could hear from their shouting that the verdicts meant nothing to them. They wanted this man's death, and nothing less would satisfy them. I saw the chief priests and elders circulating now among the rabble, whispering in a frantic manner, and suddenly the crowd began to shout as one man. "Away with this man" they screamed as if the idea had been their own. "Release Barabbas!"

I had heard of Barabbas. He was a thief and a murderer.

"We want Barabbas! We want Barabbas!" the crowd shouted, jingling the coins in their pockets, envisioning more to come.

Pilate had a beaten look on his face. A soldier handed him a note. I saw his face grow whiter and more drawn as he read it, and without a word he handed it to me. I could hardly believe what I read. It was from Claudia. Claudia, who had always put wealth and position above everything, Claudia, whose ambition had been like a lash across her husband's back! The note was not long. It said simply, "Have nothing to do with that righteous man, for I have suffered much over him in a dream." Claudia wanted

Pilate to release Jesus! I saw Pilate's face brighten, as if he had been set free from some heavy burden.

The shouting was louder now in our ears. It was like the regular beating of a drum, as they repeated over and over, "We want Barabbas! We want Barabbas!"

Pilate again asked the question he had put to them earlier. Jesus was standing beside him, and I thought that perhaps Pilate felt as I did, that they could not look upon him and ask for his death.

"Which shall I release to you now, Barabbas or Jesus?"

"Barabbas!" they screamed, remembering their instructions, remembering the money.

Pilate held up his hand. He made one more try.

"What then," he asked, "shall I do with Jesus who is called Christ?"

And they shouted the more fiercely, "Crucify him! Crucify him!"

Pilate was the judge, but he was not strong enough, even with Claudia's note in his pocket, to withstand them. But he would not give up. He asked simply, "Why, what evil has he done?"

They were not going to lose their easy religion, their easy money—these rulers of the people—and their reason was not greatly different from the reason of the rabble who wanted only not to lose their money. Pilate seemed to realize he could do nothing. He turned to me saying helplessly, "Have one of the soldiers bring me a bowl of water."

He stood before them all, and he washed his hands.

In his agitation, he cut himself on the great gold ring. He looked at the blood on his hands with horror in his face. He turned to the people and screamed, "I am innocent of the blood of this man! See to it yourselves!"

They had won! They shouted back triumphantly, "His blood be on us and on our children!"

Pilate released Jesus then to the common soldiers who surrounded the palace, and they put a purple robe around his shoulders, and plaited a crown from the thorny brambles growing on the palace walls, and pushed it down upon his brow. They

broke off a reed, and put it in his hand, and they bowed their
knees before him mockingly saying, "Hail! King of the Jews."

Pilate watched for a moment or two, and then he sent a guard
and had Jesus brought back to the judgment hall. He himself went
to the balcony and raised his hand once more. When they were
quiet, he led Jesus out before them. I think he hoped they could
not fail to see the kingliness of their prisoner, in spite of the
crumpled robe, in spite of the crown from which drops of blood
were trickling. I believe Pilate thought they could not resist the
infinite love, the sorrow, not for himself, but for them, which was
in the face of Jesus.

"Look at this man!" he literally screamed at them, as if he were
issuing a command which they would not dare disobey. It was
to no avail.

They shouted back, "We have a law, and by that law he ought
to die, because he makes himself the Son of God!"

Pilate was trembling now, from head to foot. He was afraid.
He was afraid that Jesus was the Son of God. He took Jesus by
the arm, and he led him back into the judgment hall.

"Who are you?" he demanded in a kind of desperation. But
Jesus did not answer.

"Why do you not speak to me?" Pilate shouted at Jesus as if
he had been shouting at the crowd. "Do you not know that I have
the power to release you and the power to crucify you?"

Jesus spoke then, in a voice so at variance with Pilate's desperation, so different from the strident voices of his enemies, that my
own heart was quiet. "You would have no power over me," he
said, "unless it had been given you from above. Therefore he who
delivered me to you has the greater sin."

Pilate seemed strangely comforted by Jesus' words. It was as
if he had been cleared of a charge, as if he had been exonerated.
He went upon the balcony for the last time, and when the people
saw him, they began to shout. They seemed to sense a change in
him, and they were fearful lest they lose their case even now.
They had found a better approach, and they were no longer demanding Barabbas. They were saying, "If you release this man,
you are not Caesar's friend!"

Pilate answered with some show of patience, "Shall I crucify your king?" and I thought I detected a note of sorrow in his voice.

"We have no king but Caesar!" they shouted. Those Jews, who hated the Roman government and all for which it stood, who would have joined gladly in any insurrection which they felt would be successful in freeing them from the domination of Caesar! They were pledging allegiance to Caesar so that they might have Jesus put to death!

Pilate delivered Jesus to them then, and they began the terrible journey toward the place outside the city walls, which in the Hebrew is called Golgotha, and in the Greek, Calvary, meaning the place of the skull. On that Friday morning, as they led Jesus away, it made no difference to those of us who followed in the mournful procession what name they used.

After we had gone a little way, I saw Jesus stop, and strangely enough, the four soldiers and the centurion whom Pilate had sent to carry out the death sentence did not urge him forward. They waited, as if for a royal command. I wondered if they hated their assignment, or if they were like the cruel Roman soldiers who had pressed the crown of thorns on his head and had knelt in mockery.

I pushed forward, and I could see by the roadside a group of women. I saw the tear-stained face of Elizabeth, mother-in-law to Peter, and her friend Joanna, wife of Herod's steward. I saw Hannah holding little Caleb by the hand. His eyes were wide with terror. I saw the strained, pitiful faces of Mariamne and Susanna, and with her arms around them both, Aunt Thomasina. Jesus was looking at them tenderly.

"Daughters of Jerusalem," he said to them, "do not weep for me, but weep for yourselves and for your children."

I thought of the blood-thirsty implacable mob back there in the palace courtyard who had screamed, "His blood be on us and on our children!"

Jesus moved on now, not as a conquered hero surrendering to the inevitable, but with the quiet assurance of one who carries out a program planned and perfected in the eternal councils of God.

Suddenly, as the procession started again, Caleb pulled away from his mother's restraining hand. He ran out into the road

and began to beat with his tiny fists on the legs of the centurion. "You cannot take my Jesus!" he screamed. "You let him go, you soldier you!"

I walked over to the group of women and slipped my hand through Mariamne's arm. "Come with me," I said.

I touched Susanna and motioned for her to come with us also, but she only shook her head. I knew that no matter what I said, Susanna would go to the cross.

As Mariamne and I walked through the streets of Jerusalem, it was as if we moved in some frightening dream from which we knew that we would soon awaken to find life going on as before. The sun was shining brightly now, the city stirring itself for the important day. Many of the visitors had awakened, and were out to see the sights or to prepare for the ceremonies which were to follow. As we passed the Temple, I could see the priests filing in to make their final preparations. I could scarcely believe that it was only nine o'clock. It seemed as if days had passed since the early hour when Matthew had come pounding on my door to tell me of Jesus' arrest in the garden on Mount Olivet. I found myself peering into every face as we passed along, wondering if they knew the things which had taken place, which even now were being brought to their tragic culmination outside the city walls.

One of the priests, just making his entrance into the Temple court, caught sight of Mariamne and stopped us.

My friends and I had often stood outside the amphitheater in Athens where the chariot races were held, and had wagered small sums with each other that we could tell by the faces of the men as they left the gates whether they had won their bets or lost. As I looked into the face of the sanctimonious zealot who matched his steps with ours and walked beside us, I thought to myself that this was one of the men who had won! His eyes had the identical excited, glassy look which I had seen so often, and as he talked, he rubbed his hands together in a kind of self-congratulatory ecstasy.

"Well, Mariamne," he said, "we are rid of the threat to our

God. We have wiped out evil this day. We have heard the last of this Jesus of Nazareth! This 'Son of God' is even now being nailed to a Roman cross! He could save others, but himself he could not save! His followers have disappeared—not a sign of them is to be found because we have had the Temple police searching for them."

His eyes filled with gloating, and an evil sort of triumph caused his words to fall one over the other. "We know where one of them is! We know just where one of them is! You can rest assured he will give us no more trouble. It is the man Judas. After the Sanhedrin had examined Jesus this morning, when this man saw that they were taking him to Pilate, he came into the Temple, daring to come even into the Court of the Priests where we were receiving our assignments for the day. He looked sick. His shifting eyes moved from one to the other of us, darting here and there as if he wanted help but knew not where to seek it. He had thirty pieces of silver wrapped in a dirty, crumpled rag, and he was holding it away from him, as if it were some venomous living thing.

"The priest in charge spoke sternly to him, demanding how he dared to come farther than to the Court of Israel, but this Judas did not seem to hear him. He spoke in a guttural, choked voice, saying over and over that he had sinned, that he had betrayed innocent blood. We cared nothing for that. Our need for him was ended, and we turned to the important duties of the feast day. You should have seen him, Mariamne! Whining, trembling like a whipped animal, he flung the silver pieces on the floor before us all and ran down the twelve steps descending from the Court of the Priests as if he were pursued by legions of evil spirits. The chief priest told me to follow him lest he start a riot, and I followed, but there was no tumult greater than the one in his own body.

"As this Jesus of Nazareth hangs on his cross, if he looks over to the hill on the other side of the city, he may see one of his precious followers, hanging by the neck from a crooked tree. We can settle back now, Mariamne—your father and the rest of us. We have heard the last we ever will hear of Jesus, the 'Son of God'!"

Mariamne answered him nothing, nor did I.

When he was out of sight, she raised a shocked, sad face to mine.

"Judas went to the wrong place for help," she said. "I wish he had gone to Jesus."

+   +   +

We came to the house of Nicodemus, but it seemed to me that the huge bronze gate had an eerie look, as did the trees which bordered the pathway. We sat with Mariamne's father and mother in the reception room where we had sat so often in the three years I had been in Palestine. We tried to talk. We tried to talk as if it were an ordinary day, as if nothing was happening out there on that hill shaped like a skull, but each of us knew that the other was not saying the words with which our hearts were filled.

Joseph came in just before noon, making a valiant effort to behave naturally. He spoke of the weather. He said it seemed to be clouding up over in the west.

I walked outside to the court, came back in, and said that the clouds had a threatening look, but that the sun was still shining brightly in the east.

Mariamne's mother went into the back of the house, and returned with a tray of silver goblets filled with cooled crushed fruit. We all expressed great appreciation for her thoughtfulness, assured her that we had not eaten since the previous day and had been wishing for this very thing—and put our glasses down untouched. Nicodemus reached for a scroll of Jewish Scriptures, and began to turn idly through it.

"Read, Father," Mariamne said. "Read from Isaiah."

Nicodemus began to read. "He was wounded for our transgressions, he was bruised for our iniquities; upon him was the chastisement that made us whole, and with his stripes we are healed. All we like sheep have gone astray; we have turned every one to his own way; and the Lord has laid on him the iniquity of us all."

He laid the scroll on the table. He seemed to have come to a sudden decision.

"Joseph," he said, "you and I have turned to our own way. It has been the way of wealth and ease and position and prestige. We have believed in Jesus and we have done nothing against him, but we have done nothing for him, because we have been loath to lose those things. We must be cowards no longer. There must be something we can do which will show to the members of the Sanhedrin, to the High Priest Caiaphas and to old Annas that we believe Jesus to be indeed the Christ, the Son of God, and that even at this moment our God is laying on him the iniquity of us all."

Even as he spoke, the storm broke over the city. It was the hour of noon, but the sky turned as black as midnight. Nicodemus' house, a great, strong structure built of huge white stones, trembled and shook like a tent in the midst of a summer gale. From noon until three it was black dark. We spoke of having the servants light the lamps but decided against it for fear of fire.

One of the menservants who had been in the city when the storm broke, came running in, terrified and breathless, saying that the Temple had been shaken so that the beautiful veil which separated the Holy Place from the Holy of Holies was rent from the top to bottom. "It is an evil omen," he muttered repeatedly. "It is because they have murdered the Son of God."

When the storm had spent itself, Susanna came in. She was drenched from the downpour, and her clothes were whipped about her like tattered rags. There was no despair in her face but deep concern. "I cannot understand it," she said. "Aunt Thomasina and I have searched everywhere, and we cannot find my father or any of the men. Only a few minutes after they led Jesus away, Aunt Thomasina talked to Thomas for a moment and she said he was consumed with fear. He told her that he and my father and the others were certain the authorities would search them out, give them the same hurried trial and the same monstrous death they had decreed for Jesus. She said they had a hiding place but that he would tell her nothing except that wherever they were, the doors would be closed and locked for fear of the Jews. I cannot believe that my father would be afraid.

"Only a few hours remain until the setting of the sun and the beginning of the Sabbath day. The families of the two criminals who were crucified on either side of Jesus have already come to Calvary and are waiting for the soldiers to hasten their dying so that they can take them down. They know the law that no body may hang on the cross on the Sabbath day. Aunt Thomasina is big and strong. She says if we cannot find the men, she will lift Jesus from the cross, but we know it would not be possible."

"Aunt Thomasina!"

"Yes. She watched him die. She has seen the strength she demands. There is no more doubt in her heart."

Nicodemus and Joseph were looking at each other strangely. They rose as one man, and started for the outer door. As they reached it, Nicodemus turned back to those of us in the room. He walked to Susanna and put his hand on her wet shoulder.

"Have no fear, my child," he said. "Joseph has a new grave in which no man has lain. We will go to Pilate, Joseph and I. Joseph and I will take Jesus down from the cross."

I watched them go out the door. I knew that at that moment they were turning their backs on wealth, on position, perhaps on safety itself. But I had seen the sudden happiness in their faces. They had found something to do for Jesus.

+   +   +

Saturday. The Jewish Sabbath. A day which seemed as strange as the night had been, when before the dawn I left the tossed covers and the crumpled and beaten pillows of my couch to climb the stair to the north parapet of the Tower Antonia.

I glanced briefly at the low hill outside the city wall where three empty crosses stood, and turned away.

All through the night strange memories had tugged and pulled at me, each more insistent than the other. The events of Friday had played themselves out again and again against the blackness and would not let me go. I could well have believed that they were the events of a week—or a year—ago, so long had been the night, so filled with conflicting emotions.

A sweet new joy had hovered about me like a shining, shimmering cloud in the darkness when I thought of Mariamne and remembered the brightness of her dark eyes which the tears of the day had dimmed only a little time.

I tried to hold the picture of her in my heart and to treasure the memory of her hand upon mine and the kindness in the face of her father, but it would not stay.

I thought of Jesus—and peace, and certainty, and a great quietness filled me.

There was sadness in me because of him, but no despair. The memory of the compelling sweetness of his smile in Pilate's judgment hall overflowed me with a kind of radiance, a heart-satisfaction, deep and sure and steadfast, as of something earnestly sought-after—and found.

I wanted to hold the happiness and the radiance, but the other pictures pushed them out.

I saw the impatient anger of Aunt Thomasina because of the cowardice of her brother, and her new-found confidence in Jesus because she had seen the strength she had thought he did not have.

Over and over again I saw Susanna dragging the heavy foot as if suddenly it had become an unbearable burden when she remembered that her father had hidden and could not be found.

Against the blackness I saw Peter in the high priest's courtyard, in the light of the servants' fire, cold to his bones, trying to warm himself. I heard again his swearing and cursing and his remorseful sobs.

Judas. I pictured his thin, sullen face swollen and unrecognizable as he hanged from a crooked tree, his thirty pieces of silver scattered on the Temple floor.

I saw little Caleb, beating with all the might of his small body on the legs of the centurion who led Jesus to the cross. Again, I seemed to hear his screams, "You cannot take my Jesus!" and I covered my face with my pillows.

Looking out in the dawn over the city, I thought how strange it is when one's whole world is changed, that life goes on as if nothing had happened. I looked down into the Court of the Gentiles and saw the Jews as they made preparations for their Sabbath day. I saw those whose duty it was to swing open the Gate Beautiful.

I could see two priests coming out of the Temple itself, bearing tenderly between them the rent veil which had separated the Holy

Place from the Holy of Holies and parts of the heavy draperies of blue and purple and scarlet and fine linen which had hung at the entrance. I saw that in the storm one of the great bunches of golden grapes had fallen from its golden vine. The two were followed by other priests walking two by two, walking slowly, solemnly, as if they followed a dead body.

I wanted to stand upon the parapet and shout. I wanted to call aloud to them, "Grieve not for the things of thread and cloth and metal! Grieve only that having been granted your only chance to see your God, you have put him to death!"

I heard the scraping noise of sandaled feet climbing the stair. It was Pilate. "Speak softly!" he said. "I have had all I am able to tolerate of these Jews!"

He wore a short, oblong mantle, similar to the Greek chalmys, much like the one he had worn when he received me in his private chambers almost three years earlier. Almost involuntarily, I glanced at the forefinger of his right hand. He wore no ring. On his hand was a long cut with the blood dried and hard upon it. Again I remembered Julius.

Pilate's face had lost some of its tension. He even laughed a little as he told me of his reason for coming to the parapet so early in the morning. A deputation of Jews from the Sanhedrin, he said, had already demanded an audience with him. They had come before he was out of bed with their bowing and scraping and their spurious respect.

"What could they want now?" I asked him.

They had wanted the sepulcher where Jesus lay, sealed with the imperial seal and a stone placed before it. They had wanted a guard of fully armed soldiers to keep watch.

"They are afraid, Lysias!" Pilate said. "I saw it in their faces. After they have achieved their nefarious purposes, after seeing Jesus hanging dead upon a cross, after seeing Nicodemus and Joseph of Arimathea taking him from the cross, wrapping him in the burial linens, and laying him in the tomb, they are afraid!

"They said to me, 'Sir, we remember how that imposter said, while he was still alive, "After three days I will rise again." Therefore order the sepulcher to be made secure until the third day, lest his disciples go and steal him away and tell the people,

"He has risen from the dead," and the last fraud will be worse than the first.' I answered them curtly enough. I promised the armed guard, and I told them to go themselves and make the sepulcher as sure as they could."

I thought perhaps Pilate might be wondering if they could ever make it sure enough to hold him. If death itself could hold him.

He carried a small parchment scroll in his hands. "A token of commendation for your three years of excellent service. I have had one delivered to your home in Athens. It permits you to choose your next place of service. When I had it prepared on your return from northern Palestine, I thought of it as a reward. Now I wonder if you will want to leave.

"I am not sure that I would want to leave, although I have hated this land and its people since the day I set foot on its soil. I am not sure about anything. Claudia, my high-born, ambitious wife is changed. She came from Golgotha yesterday afternoon bringing with her a group of peasant women from Galilee. Wet and bedraggled they were, and weeping in each other's arms. Last night she spoke to me with real affection in her voice. She spoke strange words. 'You did the best you could, my husband,' she said.

"Tribune, I am a man beset with thoughts beyond my understanding. I cannot rightly determine what is true and what is false."

+   +   +

It was Sunday. As it began to dawn toward the first day of the week, Zoldi called outside my door. I had been awake, remembering the previous evening, how late we had talked in the house of Nicodemus and how strange the conversation had been. Susanna was there, and Aunt Thomasina, and Joseph.

There were no tears, no words of sadness. Rather I thought there was a kind of exultation in all of us as if some mighty victory had been won, some gigantic achievement accomplished.

Joseph and Nicodemus spoke of plans for establishing a private law firm which would devote itself largely to the cases of the indigent, the oppressed, and the downtrodden of the city. The rest of us had no definite plans for any action for the future different from that in which we were engaged. We knew, however, that something was ahead. Something different from any life or any plan of life we had known.

We talked about Jesus. As we talked, it was as if his presence filled the room. It was as if we could put out our hands and touch him.

"Perhaps that could be what he meant," Mariamne said, "about rising again. Perhaps it is this nearness—this awareness that he is here—which is in our hearts, and will be forever in the hearts of believers everywhere."

"No," Susanna answered positively. "Not that alone. Tomorrow is the third day. Tomorrow Jesus will rise from the dead as he said."

"You are overwrought," Aunt Thomasina said, crossing the room and putting her hand on Susanna's brow. "My child, I think you have a fever."

"I have no fever," Susanna replied, almost stubbornly. "Jesus said that he had the power to lay down his life and the power to take it up again. I believe what Jesus said."

"In the resurrection at the last day, my child," Nicodemus said kindly.

"No," Susanna repeated. "On the morrow. I do not understand you. You say you believe in him, that you believe he is the Christ, the Son of God, and yet you do not accept his words as truth. My own father and the other men who have followed him and loved him for three years are behind closed, locked doors for fear of the Jews who put Jesus to death. All over the city there are people, people who flocked about him when he healed their sick and their blind and their lame, and now they huddle together, not speaking, not eating, not sleeping, just looking at each other with dull, expressionless eyes, as if they had come to the end of all they ever have hoped and ever have dreamed."

Susanna stood up, and her heavy foot somehow looked less helpless. "I tell you it is not true," she said. "This is not the end, it is the beginning. Mary of Magdala and some of the other women are even now preparing spices for the anointing of Jesus' dead body against the coming of the dawn. I tell you they are wrong. They ought to be preparing a robe for his living body and shoes for his feet! The whole world ought to be standing on tiptoe for the coming of the third day!"

My mind was filled with these memories as I opened the door for Zoldi. "I am glad you are awake," he said. "I have a great need to talk. I feel confused, uncertain, as if my mind were stretched and pulled by conflicting emotions and conflicting beliefs."

He told me that yesterday, all day, he had talked to the centurion who was commissioned by Pilate to lead Jesus to the cross. A hard, unfriendly man, he said he was, curt, cold and unfeeling in his response to the soldiers under him, strict and unrelenting and ruthless in his dealings with everybody. Zoldi said that yesterday the centurion would not leave his room.

It had been a lonely walk, he had told Zoldi, from the time Jesus had stopped for a moment to speak to some women by the roadside, until they had reached the place of the skull. Two crosses were there for the criminals, Jesus carrying his own until he had stumbled under the weight. It was not a new thing to him, the crucifying.

Many times he had raised the hammer and driven the nails into outstretched hands and feet. Many times he had heard the agonizing screams. Many times he had stood to watch men die. His very hardness had made him well fitted for the business to be accomplished, the assignment all men shunned.

"Now," Zoldi said, "he repeats it over and over again, 'Truly this was the Son of God!'"

The man had wakened Zoldi while it was yet dark, saying he was going to Calvary, that he must be there before the day broke. He must be there, he had said, when Jesus rises from the dead.

Zoldi brushed his hand across his eyes. "This man is no Jew, Lysias," he said. "He is not one easily moved or changed in his mind. He is never moved by his emotions. And yet he believes that when this day dawns, Jesus will come forth alive, that there will be need for whatever service he can render."

As Zoldi was speaking, I began to hear excited voices in the courtyard. We ran down the stairs, and in the dim light of the early morning I saw Mariamne and Susanna and Aunt Thomasina

—and Claudia, wife of Pontius Pilate. In the dimness, their faces looked as if the sun were shining on them.

"Hurry, Claudius!" Mariamne called excitedly. "Some of the women have been to the sepulcher. The stone has been rolled away! The huge stone which the Jewish rulers had placed before the tomb! It was rolled away, Claudius, and the Roman soldiers whom Pilate ordered there, at the insistence of a delegation from the Sanhedrin, were lying on the ground in a dead faint! Their shining swords lay beside them."

Claudia took up the story. "The women were afraid! They ran to tell the men, and they met Jesus on the way."

"It is true!" I heard the exultation in the voice of Susanna. "It is as I believed! Jesus Christ is risen as he said!"

"Jesus spoke to them," Mariamne continued. "He used no strange words. He spoke to them as if he never had been away, the greeting which is used a thousand times in the public market place."

An expression of sadness suddenly covered Susanna's face as if it were covered by a cloud. "The men would not believe them," she said. "My father and the others thought that the things the women said were idle tales. But they believe now! First Peter and John, and then my father and the others, ran to the tomb. They saw that it indeed was empty. They saw the long, intricate wrappings of linen which Nicodemus and Joseph had wrapped about the body of Jesus, and the napkin which had been wrapped about his head, lying separately. Nothing had been disturbed! It is as he said! Christ Jesus is risen from the dead!"

Letter from Lysias

Claudius Lysias, Servant of Jesus Christ . . .
To his father, the Most Excellent Marcus Lysias, teacher of philos-
ophy in the city of Athens, Greece . . .
Greetings to you and to my dearly loved mother:

Seven weeks have gone by since I wrote the last words of the report I promised. It has been a wonderful and an incredible seven weeks. We have seen Jesus alive again. We have seen the nail-prints in his hands and in his feet, and the wound in his side. We have seen him eating with his disciples, and have heard him as he talked and taught, just as he did before that tragic Friday when they nailed him to a Roman cross.

And now he has left them. It was nine days ago, when I had visited the house of Martha and Mary and their brother Lazarus, and had started walking the two miles across the Mount of Olives to the city of Jerusalem, that I came upon a strange group of men. They stood gazing steadfastly into the heavens, and at first I did not recognize them—Matthew and Philip and John and James and Peter and Thomas and Nathanael and the others.

They would walk with me they said. Jesus had left them now, but he had told them to go to Jerusalem and to wait. He had spoken of a new power which would come upon them.

They wanted to get back to Galilee, to take up the lives they had known, but Jesus had said they were to witness for him, not only in the great city of Jerusalem, but in the province of Judea, the province of Samaria, and to the uttermost parts of the earth. They must wait. Something was ahead.

My heart filled with apprehension as I looked at them. I wondered if it was to be in the gnarled and work-worn hands, the uneducated minds, the slow-to-believe hearts of those eleven men that Jesus was leaving all he had hoped and planned for the world. They were my friends, but the best anyone could say for them was that in the time he lay in the tomb they had wept and mourned and had hidden themselves behind closed and locked doors. When the women had come to say that Jesus was risen from the dead, they thought the things they were saying were as idle tales. They knew now that he had risen, but as I looked at them plodding along the mountain path, for the first time since I had seen Jesus led away to the cross I was overwhelmed with the waste, the uselessness of it all. For the first time there came over me a feeling of defeat, as if his enemies had won after all, as if his living and his dying had been for naught.

I must find Mariamne, I told myself, as soon as we came into the city walls.

When we were in the familiar reception room, I began to tell her of my fears. "What will happen now, Mariamne?" I asked her. "This is such a tiny land, those eleven men are so weak, so uncertain, and it is upon them that belief in Jesus as the Son of God must depend. Jesus has told them to wait, that they are to receive some new power, but waiting is hard. Suppose they grow impatient and restless, and will not wait. Suppose they begin to realize that such an undertaking as Jesus has envisioned would take money, and influence in high places. Suppose they realize they cannot do it—not without him. Suppose they give up and go back to their fishing and farming and tax-gathering, and the three glorious years he lived and the death he died become only a pleasant legend in this land of Palestine, and people in the whole world who live today, and who will live in centuries to come, never hear of him!"

Mariamne knelt down in front of me and took both my hands in hers.

"Listen to me, Claudius," she said quietly. "It is a terrifying and a glorious thing to realize that Jesus Christ, the Son of God, who is from everlasting to everlasting, who created this little earth, and could blot it out as you and I might blot up a bit of spilled milk—Jesus Christ needs men! He has chosen those eleven who seem to you and to me to be so weak and uncertain and inefficient, and he could not be mistaken. He sees in them potentialities which we cannot see, which they themselves do not realize. He needs them, and they will not fail.

"The earthly kingdom, the earthly power, for which they hoped is never to be. From this day forward, to be a follower of Jesus Christ in Palestine will involve wandering and persecution, imprisonment, and perhaps death, but they will not turn back. Jesus needs men and women to carry forward his plans for all mankind today, and I think he will always need them. I think he needs you, Claudius, and I think he needs me."

My heart was quiet. I leaned and kissed Mariamne gently on the lips.

As I write I try to picture your faces. Do you doubt the validity of the things I have written?

You, my father, who love wisdom for wisdom's sake, with your deep insight into that science which investigates the principles of reality, and you, my mother, with your gentle rearing, your sheltered life. Do you doubt that the man who taught here for three unforgettable years, who died a shameful death on a Roman cross outside the city gates, is indeed the Christ, the Son of God?

Do either of you doubt it?

You must not dare to doubt it!

Let me add one inescapably convincing chapter—about my friends, Matthew and the others, the eleven men who were with Jesus for those years, who heard his words, who saw his power, and who, when the test came, were weak and cowardly and unbelieving.

I have seen those men today.

Picture yourself here with me, in this city of Jerusalem where, not more than seven weeks ago, the arrest, the trial, and the crucifixion took place. Nothing is changed. The same men are in the high places of the Sanhedrin. High Priest Caiaphas is there, and his evil old father-in-law, Annas, and all their kin. They have not changed, unless they have grown more bitter, more frustrated.

Although they have succeeded in bringing about the death of Jesus, they have not been able to wipe out belief in him and in his teachings.

Go with me inside the palace of Caiaphas where a meeting of the Sanhedrin is in progress. Peter and John have been arrested. They have healed a lame man outside the Gate Beautiful, and the city is in an uproar.

Watch them with fear in your heart. Watch Peter, who said of Jesus—cursing and swearing—"I never even knew the man!" Watch John, whose strength has not yet been put to the test. Fear with me that this may be the end.

Listen to Caiaphas as he demands with anger in his voice, "By what power or by what name did you do this?"

Draw a deep breath as Peter answers. "In the name of Jesus Christ of Nazareth, whom you crucified, whom God raised from the dead! It is by him that this man is standing before you well."

Watch them now as they send Peter and John from the room, and begin whispering, then talking louder and louder as they connive together as to what they ought to do. There is desperation in their cruel faces as they say, "What shall we do with these men? For that a notable sign has been performed through them is manifest to all the inhabitants of Jerusalem, and we cannot deny it. Perhaps if we threaten them, they will remember their leader! Call them back!"

Let your nails cut into your palms. Tremble as you realize that those two men will remember the terror, that they will remember the agony! Hear Caiaphas as he says, "We charge you that you do not speak or teach any more in the name of Jesus!"

Say yourself that this is the end.

Let shame come into your heart, and tears to your eyes, that you could have doubted them. Hear them as they answer. "We cannot but speak of what we have seen and heard!"

Follow them as they return to the others. Let apprehension stir again as you remember that these are only two, the rest may not be so strong. Listen as they ask eagerly, "What did they say? What did they do?" Hear Peter and John as they recount the threats.

Stand very still as they begin to pray. Expect that you will hear them say, "Protect us from these, our enemies! Keep us safe! Deliver us from the terrifying things which happened to Jesus!"

Let your heart sing with wild exultation as you hear their words.

"Sovereign Lord, who didst make the heaven and the earth and the sea, and everything in them! The kings of the earth have stood against your Son Jesus, even Herod, and Pontius Pilate, with the Gentiles and the people of Israel. And now, Lord, behold their threatenings against us, and grant that we may speak with all boldness!"

Let your heart tell you that you are witnessing the greatest of all miracles. The miracle of eleven men who were afraid and now are filled with courage, who were weak and now are towers of strength. Eleven men who will speak with all boldness! Eleven men who will turn the world upside down!

I, Claudius Lysias, have seen the things which they have seen. I have heard the things which they have heard.

I, too, must speak with all boldness!